FAIRLIE'S SECRET WAR

FAIRLIE'S SECRET WAR

HOW ONE VILLAGE HELPED DEFEAT THE GERMAN U-BOATS

JOHN RIDDELL

ORIGIN

To Anne

First published in Great Britain in 2022 by
Birlinn Ltd

West Newington House
10 Newington Road
Edinburgh
EH9 1QS

www.birlinn.co.uk

Reprinted 2022

ISBN: 978 1 83983 023 5

British Library Cataloguing-in-Publication Data
A catalogue record for this book is available on request from the British Library

Typeset by Initial Typesetting Services, Edinburgh
Printed and bound in Malta by Gutenberg Press

CONTENTS

PREFACE

I came to live in Fairlie in 1972. The small Ayrshire Coast village was not unknown to me, as in my younger days I had often boarded Clyde steamers at Fairlie's wooden pier for summer holidays on the islands of Bute and Arran. Having a keen interest in all things related to the Clyde and its shipping, I was also aware of the William Fife & Son boatyard, famous throughout the sailing world for the design and construction of beautiful racing yachts. After making my home in the village I made occasional visits to the Bay Street yard to watch the skilled craftsmen building and repairing the boats. Like many others living in Fairlie, I was saddened when the 180-year-old boatyard finally closed.

Over the years I occasionally heard older Fairlie residents talk of what they called 'The Establishment'. It was part of the Navy, I would be informed, and occupied the Fife yard during the Second World War. Something to do with submarines, those villagers who still recalled it said, but always adding that the activities were very, very secret. Not even the locals who worked there, one elderly man told me, really knew much about what was going on.

In Fairlie Parish Church there is a small wall plaque commemorating six Royal Navy sailors who were drowned close to the village in 1944. They were part of the crew of a warship called HMS *Kingfisher*. I have to say I had taken little notice of this plaque on my visits to the church. With my known interest in ships, however, a few years ago I was asked if I would write a short article about the plaque's history for the church newsletter. So I started to research the story of not only HMS *Kingfisher*, but also why HMS *Kingfisher* was at Fairlie during the war.

I eventually discovered that the official title of the wartime occupant of the Bay Street yard was His Majesty's Anti-Submarine Experimental Establishment Fairlie. It was part of the Royal Navy and it was based in the village from October 1940 until February 1946. As the name indicates, it was a place where experiments were carried out into ways of opposing submarines, or as the German ones were called, U-boats. But what kind of experiments and what did they involve? I was told that many very clever people were employed there. Who were these people and where did they come from? Fairlie in 1940 was quite a small village. How did those who lived there react to the five years of secret research carried on within their community?

I hope I have provided answers to these and many more questions in the following pages. I have been fascinated by what my research has discovered. The experimental work undertaken at Fairlie did indeed make a major contribution to Britain not losing the battle against the U-boats. More intriguingly, it also formed the basis of much of the pro- and anti-submarine research activity of the later Cold War years, which is no doubt why everything to do with the Establishment was locked away in the National Archives out of reach until 1975.

There have been many books written about the battle between the Royal Navy and the U-boats during the Second World War. These range from the personal accounts of those who fought in that battle to very technical and detailed descriptions of the techniques and weaponry of anti-submarine warfare. In writing this history of the Establishment I have drawn extensively on the content of a number of these books, particularly with regard to the equipment developed first to find and then to sink the U-boats.

Those undertaking any form of research must strike a balance, a compromise. On the one hand there is the desire to discover more and more about your subject, to explore further avenues, even cul-de-sacs. On the other hand, there is the reality of finite time and having to come to a conclusion, to say 'enough'. I hope that my decision regarding when to say enough has been made at the right time.

This story is about more than the technical developments of Second World War anti-submarine warfare and Fairlie's role in these. It is also a local story. It is a story about people and a small seaside village, and how that village played host to a very secret establishment that made a major contribution to winning the Second World War.

John Riddell

ACKNOWLEDGEMENTS

It has been challenging to discover all of the factual information contained in this history. In addition to the specific references listed, a prime source has been the National Archives at Kew and I thank its search staff for the helpful way in which they responded to my numerous emailed requests.

The files of the local newspaper, the *Largs & Millport Weekly News*, contain useful references to what was going on in Fairlie, albeit ones heavily restricted by wartime censorship.

A wide range of sources have provided the images in the text and these are acknowledged where known. I am particularly grateful to the Imperial War Museum, the National Library of Scotland, the Scottish Maritime Museum, the Clyde River Steamer Club and the relatives of those who served at Fairlie for this assistance.

Many people worked at the Establishment. As will be explained in the following pages, the highly secret nature of the research meant that very few were able to talk or write about what they did, saw or heard. The passing of the years has also meant that there are now very few people still alive who could provide, through meetings or by correspondence, a direct memory of that wartime service. I am very grateful to those who have assisted.

My fellow members of the North Ayrshire Family History Society and the Largs and District Historical Society have provided advice, support and assistance, which is much appreciated.

No history can be written today without reference to the Internet. What a service the creator of that resource has provided to the twenty-first-century researcher!

At Birlinn, Mairi Sutherland has provided much advice. I am very grateful to her for her patient assistance and understanding.

Chapter 1

INTRODUCTION

'an unfair and underhand way to fight'

It is October 1940. Britain has been at war with Germany for just over a year. An old grey bus with wooden seats arrives in the Ayrshire coastal village of Fairlie and finds its way into Bay Street. It stops outside the entrance to the world-famous yacht building yard of William Fife & Son, closed down since 1939. Fourteen men get off the bus and go into the yard. A notice goes up. It states that the yard has been requisitioned by the Admiralty for the duration of the war. Within days it is a scene of great activity, leading to much local speculation as to what is going on. His Majesty's Anti-Submarine (A/S) Experimental Establishment Fairlie had come into being.

The story of what was generally referred to in Fairlie as simply 'the Establishment' started during the First World War. On 5 September 1914 – just one month after Britain had declared war on Germany – the Royal Navy cruiser HMS *Pathfinder* was torpedoed by a German submarine, or U-boat (from the German *Unterseeboot*), near the entrance to the Firth of Forth. By chance the torpedo hit the cruiser's magazine, causing a huge explosion. Two hundred and sixty-one of her crew died as the nine-year-old warship disappeared. Three weeks later, three more British cruisers were sunk off the Dutch coast in less than an hour by another U-boat's torpedoes. With alarming suddenness the Royal Navy had been made acutely aware of sea warfare's new and very dangerous dimension.

1

A contemporary German postcard marking the sinking of HMS *Aboukir*,
HMS *Cressey* and HMS *Hogue* by a U-boat commanded by Otto Weddigen;
1,459 crew members of the three cruisers lost their lives.

At the outbreak of the First World War, Britain's Royal Navy was the
largest and most powerful in the world. Its historic role was to protect
the country's shores from attack and to ensure that Britain's vast sea
trade, on which the country and its empire were so dependent, could
continue without interruption. The great might of the Royal Navy
centred on its fleet of eighteen battleships based on the design of the
revolutionary HMS *Dreadnought*, built in 1906. These large, powerfully
gunned and well-protected vessels were all of recent construction and
were supported by ten battlecruisers, as well as by a large number of
smaller cruisers to seek out the enemy, and by even more destroyers
which in close engagement could let loose torpedoes. The potential
enemy was seen as Germany, which had also built up a formidable, but
less numerous, fleet with the same objectives. Future battles between
these adversaries were envisaged by both navies as being little different
from that of Trafalgar and the Nile around a century before. The range

2

would be very much greater and the firepower much more deadly, but it would still be two fleets of ships bombarding each other to destruction or retreat. The North Sea was seen as the most likely location for such a battle.

The main offensive task given to the Royal Navy from the outset of the First World War was to prevent merchant ships carrying food and raw materials to Germany by using its warships to enforce a blockade within the waters of the North Sea. Both German and neutral vessels were stopped, searched and, if found to be carrying cargo for Germany, seized. But Britain as an island nation was also heavily dependent upon sea trade for food and raw materials and for the oil fuel now increasingly needed by some of the new warships. Might it not also be vulnerable to a blockade of its shipping?

The western approaches to the British Isles from the Atlantic are very much larger in area than those leading through the North Sea and English Channel to Germany. For a blockade of Britain to have any chance of success, Germany would need to deploy a high proportion of its available battleships and cruisers to cover this area. Potentially thinly spread out, the warships would be highly vulnerable to attack by the battleships of the much larger Royal Navy. Thus the German government took the decision to use its submarines – at first intended only to attack British warships such as HMS *Pathfinder* – to intercept and if necessary sink the merchant ships carrying cargoes to Britain. Deploying its fleet of U-boats would involve much less risk than a potentially decisive surface ship battle and, if carried out in sufficient strength, could act as a counter to the British blockade of Germany. The U-boats took on this new role of stopping and sinking British merchant ships in February 1915. So effective were the subsequent attacks that by the end of September of that year some 480 British cargo ships had been sunk by an average of just seven U-boats at sea at any one time.

At first the U-boats gave warning of an attack on a merchant ship, and only when the ship's crew were safely in lifeboats was the ship sunk by gunfire or by the placement of an explosive charge. But this was a

On finding a ship sailing on its own, the U-boat's attack was normally
conducted in daylight. In April 1917 the British steamer *Maplewood* was on
a voyage from North Africa to Hartlepool with a cargo of iron ore when it
was intercepted by *U-35* near Sardinia. The crew were given time to leave
the ship, after which she was sunk by a single torpedo.

dangerous procedure for the U-boat, particularly as the ships being
intercepted began to be armed, and Germany soon announced that it
would regard all of the sea around the British coast as a war zone, and
that British ships within that zone would be sunk, usually by torpedo,
without warning.

One of the early casualties of that announcement was the passenger
liner *Lusitania*. Part of the Cunard Line's transatlantic fleet, this magnificent four-funnelled ship made regular crossings between Liverpool
and New York following her completion on the Clyde in 1907, and
these continued after the war started. However, *Lusitania* had attracted
the interest of the German government who believed that she might
be carrying military cargo on her eastbound crossings. She was thus
considered to be a legitimate target for a U-boat attack.

Aware that citizens of the still-neutral United States were crossing the Atlantic on the liner, the German Embassy in Washington placed a warning in American newspapers that such British vessels could be sunk on sight. But the warning was not fully heeded and on the afternoon of 7 May 1915, when nearing the Irish coast, *Lusitania* was hit by a torpedo fired by the small submarine *U-20*. The great liner sank quickly, taking to their deaths some 1,195 of her passengers and crew. United States citizens were among those lost, and the disaster was one of the factors that caused the US to join the war against Germany.

As the land war progressed with no obvious conclusion, the German government decided to increase the attacks on the ships carrying supplies to Britain. In February 1917 it announced a policy of unrestricted submarine warfare, claiming the right to attack without warning any ship sailing within the waters approaching and around the British Isles.

The *Lusitania* passed down the River Clyde from John Brown's Clydebank shipyard on 27 June 1907. At that time she was the largest completed ship in the world. A high-water depth of 35 feet was needed along the 15-mile-long channel for her safe passage to the Tail of the Bank anchorage.

Some fifty U-boats were then deployed in the Atlantic and North Sea with the result that within six months 3.5 million tons of British and neutral ships had been sunk. Such a rate of loss of ships and their cargoes meant that there was a very real possibility that Britain's ability to continue to support the troops in France might be in doubt. If food supplies to its population came near to causing starvation, the government would have no option but to seek a peace with Germany by the end of the year. Only the introduction of the convoy system of guarding merchant ships prevented these dire predictions becoming a reality before the land war finally brought peace on 11 November 1918. Up to that date the U-boats had sunk approximately 7,500 ships of all types.

A First World War U-boat. In 1914 the German Navy had twenty-four U-boats in its fleet. By 1918 there were 134, but during the course of the war 178 were lost to anti-submarine forces.

The sinking of its four cruisers in 1914 showed the Royal Navy that the submarine was a very different weapon from the powerful battleships and battlecruisers which the Navy foresaw as being its great strength at the start of the war. It did not appear over the horizon to engage in a mighty gun fight. The first a surface ship was aware that it was under attack was usually the explosion of the torpedo fired at it. And where had the attack come from? There was no ship to be seen as the submerged submarine made its escape. As one admiral exclaimed angrily: 'It was an unfair and underhand way to fight.' But another young officer stated more bluntly: 'I really don't think the Navy knew what it was doing at this stage: it hadn't been at war for years.' Irrespective, the U-boat was clearly a very effective way of sinking British ships and means had to be found to locate and destroy the submarine both before it could mount an attack, and after it had disappeared to await another target. Thus the skills and techniques collectively known as anti-submarine warfare came into being.

But how do you find a submerged submarine, and how then do you destroy it? As the public became more aware of the submarine attacks, many suggestions were made to the Admiralty as to ways the U-boats could be located and sunk. Among those given some initial consideration was a proposal to train seagulls to detect and follow a submarine by associating the raised periscope with the availability of food. Another involved sea lions. After initial experiments carried out in one of Glasgow's public baths, it was found that a sea lion could detect an underwater noise similar to that of a submarine over a distance of up to three miles. But persuading the mammals to be more interested in U-boats than in shoals of fish proved to be an insurmountable challenge. Somewhat more realistic were plans for fishing vessels to drag strong steel nets through the seas where U-boats might be expected, and for fast destroyers to tow a heavy explosive charge which would detonate on hitting a U-boat. While both of these actions were implemented in high-risk areas such as the Firth of Forth, there is no recorded evidence of either resulting in the sinking of a U-boat.

The transmission of sound through water is part of the science known as acoustics. Sound passes quite easily through water and about four times faster than it passes through air. If the noise made in the sea by, say, a propeller turning could be detected by some form of device able to listen for that noise then a warning might be given of a submarine's presence even when it was fully submerged. That device was the hydrophone.

As sound passes through water it causes very small changes in the water pressure. The hydrophone when placed in the water experiences these changes and, through the resulting oscillation of a small quartz disc, converts the pulses into an electrical signal. At a shore station or on a ship or submarine, the electrical signal is made audible. With experience, the nature of the noise provides the listener with an indication of the source of the sound, for example a shoal of fish or a ship's propeller, while the strength or loudness of the noise can give an indication as to how close to the hydrophone the source of the noise might be.

Pioneering research on use of the hydrophone for detecting underwater noise had been initiated by the British government in the 1880s and accelerated as the U-boat threat increased after 1914. To gain greater understanding of its potential for the detection of submarines, the Admiralty set up a number of research establishments. In Scotland the main ones were at Hawkcraig Point near Aberdour on the Firth of Forth and at Shandon on the Gare Loch arm of the Firth of Clyde. Hawkcraig was established in 1915 and very quickly developed into one of the Royal Navy's most important hydrophone research establishments of the First World War. It was also the training centre for those operating the shore listening stations which monitored the lines of hydrophones being laid on the seabed at the entrance to important harbours to detect the passage of any U-boat. These First World War hydrophone arrays included one on the Clyde which extended from Wemyss Bay across to the Cowal shore. The history of the Hawkcraig establishment is described in Diana Maxwell's book *Listen Up!*

The research station at the small village of Shandon on the east side of the Gare Loch occupied the building and extensive grounds of West Shandon House, first constructed as a seaside mansion by the Clyde shipbuilder Robert Napier. After his death in 1876 it was redeveloped as one of Scotland's leading hydropathic hotels. Under the name Shandon Hydro it continued as such until it was requisitioned in 1918 by the Clyde Anti-Submarine Committee, one of several regional groups established by the government to co-ordinate local research work. Selected by the Admiralty to be the main postwar experimental station for underwater acoustics, it operated as Admiralty Experimental Station Shandon from February 1919 until January 1921 when post-armistice budget cuts resulted in its closure. Although Shandon had a very short life, the scientists who worked there undertook valuable research, and the young men who developed their knowledge and experience of underwater acoustics in the sheltered waters of the Gare Loch were among those who, twenty years later, were to come to work at Fairlie. After a return to civilian use, West Shandon House was demolished in 1957. Today the former grounds are part of the Royal Navy's Faslane submarine base.

It was at the Admiralty's underwater research establishment located at Harwich in Essex that the first successful trials took place of an acoustic device which could actively transmit a sound signal and also receive an echo from a submerged object which intercepted that signal, rather than passively wait for the occurrence of an underwater noise – which is what the hydrophone did. Conceived by the Canadian-born electrical engineer Reginald Fessenden as a means of transmitting underwater messages to ships, the concept of identifying a submerged object from a reflected echo gained impetus following the *Titanic*'s 1912 iceberg collision. After observing successful trials of such a transmitter/receiver in France in 1916, the value of the technique for actively detecting U-boats was quickly realised by the Admiralty.

Extensive research and development was instigated at Harwich. By March 1918 the scientists there, led by the Canadian Professor Robert

Boyle, were able to demonstrate a trial which showed echoes being received from a submarine over 1,500 feet away from the sound beam transmitter. By the end of the war a device had been sufficiently developed both to send a supersonic sound wave through the water and to receive a return echo from any reflecting object. Most importantly, by noting the time between the outgoing and incoming sound waves, a calculation could be made of the distance of the echo source from the transmitter. The direction of the echo source could also be estimated by noting the change in the strength of the echo as the transmission angle was altered. After further trials the first prototype of the new submarine detecting device was fitted to the former fishing vessel *Hiedra* in August 1918, and early in 1919 to the small warships HMS *P59*, HMS *Cachalot* and HMS *Osprey*, which were part of the Royal Navy's newly formed 1st Anti-Submarine Flotilla.

To maintain secrecy about the principles of the new detection technique, the Admiralty coined the description 'asdic'. Despite later assertions about what the letters stood for, it is now accepted that asdic was a meaningless word taken from the informal name – 'the asdics' – given to those who worked in the **A**nti-**S**ubmarine **D**ivision of the department then responsible for these activities. The word first appeared in print in July 1918 as a replacement for the term 'supersonic'. However, such was the potential importance of asdic that no public reference to the term was permitted until 1929, and even after that date Royal Navy warships fitted with asdic were instructed to keep the equipment covered when any visitors were aboard. Asdic continued to be the term used by the Royal Navy until the 1950s when it was gradually replaced by the American word 'sonar'. For the purposes of the Establishment's story, however, asdic will be the term used throughout.

By the end of the First World War as many as thirty different British government establishments were engaged in anti-submarine research and development work. Such a scattered approach often meant that one group of scientists was not aware of similar research being carried

HMS *Icewhale* was built as an anti-submarine coastal patrol vessel in 1915
and in 1919 was one of the first Royal Navy warships to be fitted
with asdic apparatus. She was later renamed HMS *Osprey*.

out by another group elsewhere in the country. In 1925 the Admiralty
accepted a government inquiry recommendation that the new
Admiralty Research Laboratory at Teddington in Middlesex, opened
in 1921 as a successor in part to Shandon, should be responsible for
the fundamental research into underwater acoustics, while all practical
research and experimental work should be centred at the Royal Navy's
base at Portland in Dorset. Situated in Weymouth Bay, Portland had
been a Royal Navy base since 1845 and in 1917 had become the home
of a school set up to train naval officers and ratings (a rating is a person
serving in the Royal Navy who is not an officer) in the use of hydrophone techniques.

The effect of that decision was that Teddington would operate as
an Admiralty research establishment under the direction of a civil service scientist, with Royal Navy officers serving there acting only in a
liaison role. Meanwhile Portland would be a Royal Navy experimental
establishment with the scientific staff working there being under the

direction of a Royal Navy captain. That at least was the intention, although as will be seen later the conflict between fundamental and applied research was to continue within the Admiralty and the Royal Navy for many more years to come.

The asdic training at Portland included practical experience with the ships of the 1st Anti-Submarine Flotilla. One of these warships was HMS *Osprey*, formerly the 1919 asdic trial ship HMS *Icewhale* mentioned above. It has been suggested that she was renamed *Osprey* by the officer then in charge of anti-submarine activity at Portland, Captain Tillard. The reason for this highly unusual action is not known, but it may be that as the officer had served during the First World War on the Clyde-built destroyer HMS *Osprey*, later scrapped, he simply wished to continue the name. Whatever the explanation, when a further reorganisation of the Royal Navy's anti-submarine capability took place in 1927, the HMS *Osprey* name was given to the part of the Portland shore base responsible for underwater acoustic experimentation and training. The warship *Osprey* then reverted to her original name of *Icewhale* before being broken up for scrap a year later. And, so far as can be found, that is how the Navy's specialist shore establishment for anti-submarine research, development and training took the name HMS *Osprey*. While the transfer of an HMS name from a ship to a shore base was unusual, the use of HMS names for shore bases as well as for ships was a long-established practice in the Royal Navy. These shore bases are often referred to by sailors as 'stone frigates'; present-day Firth of Clyde examples are HMS *Neptune*, the Faslane submarine base on the Gare Loch, and HMS *Gannet* at Prestwick Airport.

The asdic development and training activities of HMS *Osprey* expanded greatly between the First and Second World Wars. As well as developing new types of asdic, a wide range of theoretical research into the factors affecting the speed of sound through water was carried out by the Portland scientists. By the late 1930s nearly 200 staff were engaged on this work and it was generally acknowledged that HMS *Osprey* was the world leader in the development of underwater sound transmission understanding and recording for both offensive and defensive naval purposes. Most importantly, almost all of the Royal Navy's 220 warships then intended for anti-submarine operations had been fitted with asdic equipment – more, it was estimated, than available to the rest of the world's navies combined.

Such was the Admiralty's belief in the work of the Portland scientists and the development of asdic that in 1936 the then First Lord of the Admiralty claimed that the Royal Navy's anti-submarine measures 'were eighty per cent effective' and that 'no U-boat would be safe'. This reassuring view was reinforced when, after a visit to an asdic-equipped destroyer exercising off Portland a few months prior to the outbreak of the Second World War, Winston Churchill, a former First Lord of the Admiralty, described the asdic system he observed in action as 'a marvellous achievement', adding 'the nation owes the Admiralty an inestimable debt for the faithful effort sustained over so many years in its development'.

What Churchill was not told by those demonstrating the carefully managed visit, however, was that the types of asdic then available to the Royal Navy had significant limitations and were most certainly not the 'all-seeing underwater eye' that many in the Admiralty believed them to be. The Portland scientists were well aware of these limitations, but kept their peace. As will be seen in a later chapter, much more research and development would need to be carried out, and some time would need to pass, before the Royal Navy's prewar expectations of asdic as the solution to the problem of finding a submerged U-boat were turned into an acceptable reality.

Chapter 2

TO FAIRLIE

'the English invasion of Fairlie is complete'

As the Second World War entered the summer of 1940 there was growing concern in the War Cabinet that Britain's military research establishments located in the south of England would be vulnerable to the expected German invasion, as well as to attack by enemy ships and aircraft. HMS *Osprey* at the Royal Navy's Portland base was considered to be at the highest risk. If the Portland anti-submarine research establishment was destroyed, or fell into enemy hands, it would be disastrous for the increasingly vital work of finding and sinking the expanding fleet of German U-boats. These fears were fully realised in August and September 1940 when Portland and the nearby town of Weymouth were repeatedly bombed by the Luftwaffe. One of the attacks caused considerable damage to the *Osprey* research buildings, fortunately without loss of life. With further air attacks likely, the time had come to move to a safer place.

The Firth of Clyde was a natural choice for the new home of HMS *Osprey*. The Royal Navy had been familiar with its waters for many years, and warships of all sizes had from time to time visited the Clyde's training areas and anchorages. While the major Scottish prewar naval bases at Scapa Flow, Invergordon and Rosyth were all on the North Sea side of the country, hundreds of warships from battlecruisers to submarines had been constructed over the years in the Clyde's numerous shipyards. The Clyde was also some distance away from

German-occupied Europe (although the heavy bombing of Clydebank and Greenock in the spring of 1941 demonstrated that such distance could be overcome), it had good access to the Atlantic Ocean, and it had many relatively sheltered and quiet locations along its extensive shoreline. Most importantly, the Firth of Clyde had the wide range of water depths needed for anti-submarine research and training. Areas of water 300 feet deep are common, while depths of 650 feet – close to the limit of the early Second World War U-boats – can be found in Loch Fyne. No doubt also influencing the choice was the fact that the Clyde was well known to those of the Portland scientists who had worked at Shandon at the end of the First World War.

The decision to relocate HMS *Osprey* from Portland some 600 miles north to the Clyde was quickly agreed by the Admiralty and the War Cabinet, it being strongly emphasised that the transfer must be undertaken with the minimum possible disruption to the vital work being carried out. With great effort by all concerned, the move north was completed by the end of November 1940.

Rather than relocating to a single site, *Osprey*'s Portland activities were spread over four separate Clyde coast locations, each with a different role. The Cowal Peninsula holiday town of Dunoon was selected as the site for the headquarters. Here the large West of Scotland Convalescent Home was requisitioned and took the name HMS *Osprey*. This base focused on the task of training naval officers and ratings in the techniques of finding and sinking submarines, and the use of asdic. Practical training with Royal Navy warships and Clyde-based submarines would take place at Campbeltown at the south end of the Kintyre Peninsula, where the local grammar school buildings became HMS *Nimrod*. For asdic training with motor launches able to operate in shallow coastal waters, HMS *Seahawk* was set up in the former Crinan Canal offices at Ardrishaig on Loch Fyne.

One location not available to the Portland staff was Shandon. After the fall of France, Belgium and Holland in June 1940, the Gare Loch had been identified as the site of a new war emergency port intended

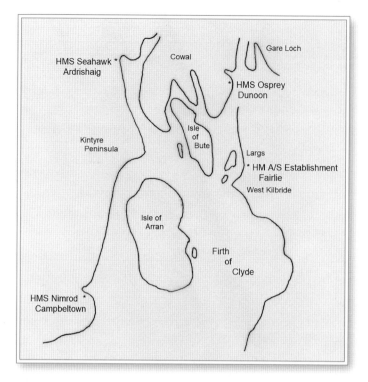

The Clyde's wartime locations of HMS *Osprey* –
Ardrishaig, Campbeltown, Dunoon and Fairlie.

to provide deep water harbour facilities should southern ports such as
London and Southampton no longer be usable by large vessels. The
noise likely from both construction and operation of the new Faslane
port, it was agreed by all, would not be compatible with experimental
work on underwater acoustics. So the experimental research came to
the small village of Fairlie on the Ayrshire Coast.

Fairlie lies between the coastal town of Largs to the north and the
inland town of West Kilbride to the south, with the Largs Channel
separating it from the two Cumbrae islands to the west. Prior to the
early years of the nineteenth century, Fairlie was not a place of any note.
In 1656, for example, it was described by Oliver Cromwell's tax com-
missioner Thomas Tucker as having 'only a few houses, the inhabitants

of fishermen, who carry fish and cattle for Ireland, bringing home corn and butter for their own use and expense'.

The two Cumbrae islands provide considerable shelter to the Fairlie shore. This not only enabled the villagers' small boats to fish and trade but also afforded a safe anchorage for the larger ships taking cargo to the other towns and villages of the Firth of Clyde and beyond. In 1759 James Watt of steam engine fame published the results of what would now be called a hydrographic survey of the Firth of Clyde undertaken by his uncle, John Watt. On the chart an anchor is shown off 'Farly', the symbol of a safe anchorage which is still in use today.

The anchorage off Fairlie was, and still is, known as the Fairlie Road. Road is a shortened form of the term 'roadstead' derived from the Middle English words 'roade', meaning riding, and 'stead', a place. Mention of the 'Fairly Road' is also made in Tucker's 1656 report, showing that the area was recognised as a safe place for a ship 'to ride to her anchor' even then.

That the Fairlie Road was a popular as well as a safe anchorage is illustrated by an article which appeared in an 1825 issue of a some-what obscure publication called the *Edinburgh Magazine and Literary Miscellany*. The author was one Andrew Allan, who described himself as a former Fairlie school teacher. In the article he recalls the village as he knew it towards the end of the eighteenth century. Referring to the Fairlie Road, he remembers having seen 'ten, yea, twenty sail of gal-lant merchantmen anchored at any one time' as they waited for better weather or the receipt of final orders from their owners before starting their next voyage. Andrew Allan also noted that while the ships lay safely at anchor off the village, 'the captain and crews caroused among us till we scarcely knew them – or one another!'

Among those who would have watched the many different ships – and maybe have been part of the carousing – was a young man called William Fife. William was one of the four sons of John Fife who had come to work as a carpenter or wright on the 4th Earl of Glasgow's Kelburn Estate, of which Fairlie was a major part. William

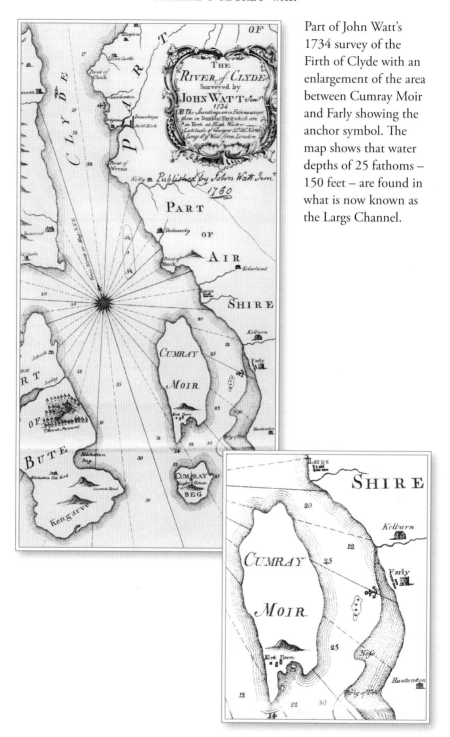

Part of John Watt's 1734 survey of the Firth of Clyde with an enlargement of the area between Cumray Moir and Farly showing the anchor symbol. The map shows that water depths of 25 fathoms – 150 feet – are found in what is now known as the Largs Channel.

was born within the estate in 1785 and as he grew up his interest in the vessels which he saw each day increased. Wishing to view them more closely, he would often borrow a small boat to row and sail around the anchored ships. He studied the different types, hull shapes and rigs, conversed with the captains and crews, and probably earned a few pennies ferrying the men to and from the shore. With the assistance of his father, and no doubt with 'spare' wood from the estate, he then built his own boat. Such was the quality of the workmanship that he was soon made an offer to purchase it. He quickly accepted and with the money received he started work on a second and then a third boat. His business prospered, and in 1803 the Earl agreed to lease him part of the foreshore at the north end of Fairlie for use as a boat building yard.

Secure in his new shoreside location, William Fife was soon constructing a variety of boats for fishing and the coastal trade, with orders coming in either directly or by recommendation as his reputation both as a designer and as a builder spread. But the Fairlie yard was not alone in the early decades of the nineteenth century, and many other boatyards and shipyards became established along the Clyde Coast to build a vast range of vessels first in wood and then in iron. Steam power was also developing. Fife did try a single steamship – the small cargo boat *Industry* of 1814 – and was offered financial backing to expand into this rapidly growing new area of work. But he resisted, and took the decision to continue as a builder of wind-driven wooden boats.

While boats for fishing and cargo carrying provided steady work, William knew that what he really wanted to do was build boats able to sail faster and have a much more attractive appearance than these sturdy working craft. But who wanted such a boat? Fortunately, William Fife was not the only person to be granted a lease of the Fairlie shore by the Kelburn Estate. The village's sheltered location and sandy beaches began to attract visitors from beyond Ayrshire. Among these visitors were some very rich Glasgow men who, as in so many places along the Clyde at this time, began to seek sites for a summer residence away from the grime and disease of the city. While part of the wealth had its origins in the compensation paid for giving up sugar and other slave plantations in South America, both as merchants and as members of the growing number of new industrialists, they had steadily amassed considerable fortunes. Always needing income for his estate, the Earl of Glasgow readily granted feus, or titles, to these affluent incomers to the extent that by the 1850s just eight large houses – all but one still existing today – occupied two-thirds of the Fairlie shoreline.

The incomers had two advantages not available to Fairlie's long-standing residents: they had plenty of money and, during their summer months in the village, they had abundant leisure time. Like William Fife, they would watch the sailing boats coming and going in Fairlie Bay and began to think that maybe a boat intended for pleasure, rather than for trade, might provide a good healthy way to spend some of the summer. And perhaps there might also be the possibility of sailing against another boat to see which one was fastest. Who better to design and build such a boat – a racing yacht – than William Fife at his yard just along the Fairlie shore?

William had married in 1813 and he and his wife Janet had ten children. Their fourth son, born in 1821, was also named William. Apprenticed to his father, William (II) again showed the flair so important to be a good designer and builder and by the time he was eighteen he had been given responsibility for the construction of Fife yachts. At first there were not so many customers, but as the new elite – and that is what the owners of Fairlie's big new houses were – saw the attractiveness of leisure sailing, the orders for yachts started to come in. William (II)'s reputation for both designing and building what became known as 'fast and bonnie' boats soon extended well beyond the Clyde, with commissions from all around Britain, and from overseas. Employment also increased, with Fairlie men, including many members of the extended Fife family, gaining the skills and trades necessary to satisfy William's very high and exacting standards of workmanship.

William (II) in turn married and in 1857 had a single son, again called William. Like his father and grandfather, William (III) was a

A view from seaward of Fife's Fairlie boatyard as it was in the 1870s.
At least four yachts can be seen under construction on the open shore.
The prominent two-storey building is Croftend House, the home of
the second William Fife and where his son William (III) was born.

superb designer of yachts and in 1885 joined his father as a partner in
the Fairlie yard, then known as William Fife & Son. The father and son
combination was highly successful, the order book was well filled, and
over the next sixteen years the Fairlie yard completed no fewer than 181
yachts of all sizes. By 1900 the yard's foreshore site had been purchased
outright from the Kelburn Estate and more sheds and other buildings
erected to allow much of the design and building work to be carried
out away from the open shore. The adjoining road had been given the
name Bay Street. New houses, including somewhat incongruously a
four-storey block of flats, now lined the road's east side opposite the
yard, replacing the original fishermen's thatched cottages.

Contributing greatly to this expansion of both Fairlie and the Fife
yard was the arrival of the railway. As the village was well beyond the
boundary of the vast Ayrshire coalfield to the south, for most of the
nineteenth century there had been no great commercial incentive to

extend a line north from Ardrossan to West Kilbride, Fairlie and Largs. But the existence of a harbour at Largs and its potential for new steamer services to the nearby islands did eventually attract the interest of the Glasgow & South Western Railway. A proposed line was approved and by 1880 this had reached the south end of Fairlie where a new station was built. Two years later a tunnel nearly 970 yards in length extended the railway around the east side of the village to the shore on the north side. Here the railway built its own steamer pier with an integral second station. This new railhead pier was a success and soon steamers were providing train-linked ferry services from Glasgow to the islands of Cumbrae, Bute and Arran, and further on to Kintyre.

The new turbine steamer *Queen Alexandra* departing Fairlie Pier for
Arran and Kintyre in 1912. During the First World War she was requisitioned
by the Admiralty as a fast troop transport and in May 1918 she rammed and
sank the mine-laying U-boat *UC-78* off Cherbourg – the only Clyde steamer
to sink a U-boat in either the First or Second World War. Later renamed
Saint Columba and given a third funnel, she remained in service with David
MacBrayne Ltd until 1958.

The arrival of the railway with its two stations and pier transformed Fairlie. The population increased from around 300 in 1871 to about 500 in 1891 as the ease of travel to and from other towns brought new families to live in the village – and allowed local men and women to obtain daily employment outwith the village. During the summer the number of holiday visitors soared, while the numerous ferry services from the pier were augmented by very popular day cruises around the Firth of Clyde. As well as the passenger traffic, Fairlie Pier also attracted a large trade in Clyde-caught herring, with the fish landed being sent on by special trains to markets as far away as London.

William Fife & Son made much use of the new railway. Timber of all types, previously floated to the shore or delivered by horse-drawn wagon, was now brought to the yard by train, as were materials like lead, brass and iron, and coal for the yard's foundries. Some of the smaller yachts could also now be delivered to their owners by rail. The railway with its frequent passenger service to Glasgow and beyond benefited the business in other ways. It gave easy access to the yard for customers and it allowed the Fifes, particularly William (III), to travel extensively to meet with prospective and established clients.

William Fife (II) died in 1902 and full control of the business passed to his forty-five-year-old son. Orders continued to be secured for yachts of all sizes. Employee numbers further increased, as did the profits from both design and building. In 1907 William (III) used part of these to construct a large new home for himself on a site over-looking his yard. Also added around this time was a novel floating dock. Fairlie's relatively flat shore made it difficult to launch yachts with deep keels, so Fife conceived the idea of first transferring them at low tide to the dock. As the tide rose, the dock's greater buoyancy floated both it and the yacht aboard, and the dock was then towed off to deeper water. Here valves were opened, the dock sunk, and the yacht floated free.

While the building of yachts continued during the First World War, activity at the Bay Street yard was further increased as orders were placed by the Admiralty for a range of support craft such as motor launches and steam pinnaces. The wooden hulls of seaplanes were also constructed by the yard's skilled workers. As recognition of this con-tribution to the war effort, William (III) was appointed OBE in 1919.

The hull of the 62-foot-long yacht *Mariquita* being moved into
Fife's floating dock in 1911. These events were attended by many Fairlie
villagers, who took great pride in the boats being constructed in what was
always regarded as 'their' yard. A history of William Fife & Son can be
found in May McCallum's book *Fast and Bonnie*.

The years after the Armistice saw mixed fortunes for William Fife &
Son. The number of wealthy men able to own and run a large yacht was
much reduced, while finding sufficient experienced crew to race such
boats became a problem. Orders for new Fife yachts fluctuated. A few
lean years after the war's end were followed by a period of full work,
in turn followed by the Great Depression of the 1930s. By 1937 the
world-famous Fife yard had only three boats under construction and
by the following year new-build work had almost ceased. In 1939 the
yard's doors closed, bringing to an end a continuous 136-year period of
boat building at Fairlie by three generations of William Fife.

It is not known who first identified Fairlie and Fife's Bay Street
boatyard as the wartime site for the research and experimental part
of Portland's HMS *Osprey*, but with the threat of invasion in 1940
many military and government officials were searching throughout
Scotland for places where research and training bases of all kinds could
be relocated away from the south coast of England. At that time the
9th Earl of Glasgow was a serving officer in the Royal Navy and it

may be that a suggestion came from him. It may also have been that the yard's role in assisting the Navy during the First World War was remembered. Irrespective, it is likely that a range of factors influenced the final choice of Fairlie. The existence of a waterfront boatyard with buildings and sheds would have been a major consideration, as would have been its proximity both to the deep water of the Largs Channel and the even deeper water further out in the Firth – key requirements for asdic experimental work. The site and the nearby anchorage of the Fairlie Road were well sheltered, and the former boatyard was close to a substantial pier, both factors of importance to the undertaking of experimental work afloat.

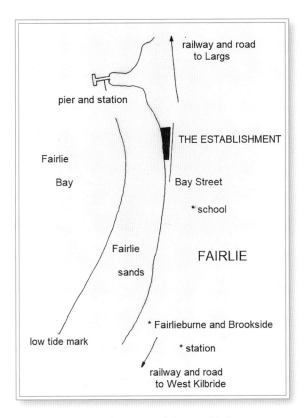

The Bay Street location of the Establishment in
the Ayrshire village of Fairlie.

Ease of communication was another factor. Unlike Dunoon, Campbeltown and Ardrishaig, Fairlie had good rail connections through its two stations and travel by staff and visitors to and from Glasgow and the country beyond would be relatively easy and quick. This was important as the work of the Establishment would require scientists from other research centres to come to Fairlie for meetings, and for staff from Fairlie to travel throughout Britain.

It is known that security also influenced the choice of Fairlie. Fairlie was still a small place in 1940, with only one road in and out. The need to continue to keep *Osprey's* anti-submarine work secret would have been a major concern to the Admiralty and watching for both spies and 'loose talk' would be much easier in a village than in a more populous town.

Bay Street, Fairlie, looking north towards the steamer pier.
The light-coloured buildings in the centre, on the sea side of the street,
are those of the William Fife & Son boatyard. The terrace of houses
beyond leads to Fairlie Pier. The tall building on the east side of
Bay Street is Fairlie's only four-storey tenement.

While the other parts of HMS *Osprey* that were moved to the Clyde were given an HMS name, Fairlie was not – it had the title His Majesty's Anti-Submarine Experimental Establishment Fairlie. Why no HMS name was given to the research part of Portland's HMS *Osprey* is not known. The secret nature of the wartime experimental work could have meant that the Admiralty did not wish to draw attention to that part of the relocated *Osprey*'s activities, although the widely circulated and regularly published Navy List – a series of confidential books detailing those serving at HM ships and shore bases – gave not only the title and address of the Fairlie site but also the phone numbers and the telegraphic address ANTISUB Fairlie. A more likely explanation is that some in the Admiralty felt that, although this was a Royal Navy establishment, the dominance of scientists rather than naval officers among those transferred to Fairlie could not justify an HMS name, and that, as with the situation at Portland prewar, what was known as 'the experimental section' should continue to work under the *Osprey* name. For whatever reason, the Fairlie research facility was described throughout the war as HM A/S Experimental Establishment Fairlie, and included in the Navy List only as a part of HMS *Osprey* at Dunoon. Unlike the First World War Shandon and Hawkcraig establishments, there is no record of the Royal Navy's White Ensign being flown at Fairlie.

The first local resident to meet Fairlie's new arrivals when they got off their bus in Bay Street in October 1940 after a three-day journey from Portland was Mr Roderick (Roddy) Graham, the Gaelic-speaking headmaster of the village school. At the start of the war he had been tasked with finding homes for children who might need to be evacuated to Fairlie in the event of Glasgow and other industrial targets being bombed. With his knowledge of where accommodation was available in the village it was natural that he was appointed the billeting officer for the fourteen weary travellers from Portland. With that task completed it was a shock to be told that 120 more people would soon be arriving from 'down south' and would also require accommodation.

It was in mid-November that a special overnight train steamed into Fairlie Pier station bringing the scientific, technical and other staff transferring from Portland to their new home in Scotland. Roddy Graham had worked wonders and by the time the train arrived some form of accommodation was available for all the new arrivals. Both single rooms and complete properties were found either by negotiation or by requisition. On 6 December the area's local newspaper, the *Largs & Millport Weekly News*, was reporting that 'the English invasion of Fairlie was complete last week', adding 'invaders and the invaded are settling down together on very friendly terms'. There was of course no mention of where the invaders had come from, or for what purpose.

Also delivered from Portland were some 200 railway wagons of machinery and experimental gear. All this equipment was moved into the Bay Street yard made ready by the advance party. A few weeks of intense activity then took place as a 137-year-old boatyard was transformed into a state-of-the-art research centre. The former upper level sail loft was made into a conference room and offices, while the large space below was divided on the Bay Street side into three rooms. One was for scientific research, the second for training, including the use of an asdic simulator, and the third for a photographic dark room and general office.

On the seaward side the whole space was converted into a well-equipped workshop in which the scientists 'lash ups' would be turned into workable prototypes for testing. In the centre of this area a large steel tank able to contain a water depth of 8 feet was constructed – water being an essential component of underwater acoustics. Three more laboratories, a drawing office and a print room for plans were added. Elsewhere other buildings were converted or constructed to provide further workshop and storage space and what was termed a propeller laboratory – of which more later. An administrative office, kitchen, eating area and toilets were added. Also installed were powerful electricity generators, electric-powered tools never having been accepted by William Fife & Son. Outside of the Bay Street site on open ground opposite, a substantial canteen was erected to provide meals for the Establishment's staff.

Any remaining boatyard equipment was shifted to a shed at the north end of the site while the two Fife yachts that were still under construction when the boatyard closed in 1939 – *Flica II* and *Madrigal* – were moved into a far corner of this building. Only the former survived her wartime layup, *Madrigal* being found to have extensive dry rot. A third yacht which was almost complete in 1939 – *Solway Maid* – was launched by her owner and taken south before the Admiralty's arrival in Fairlie. Special permission for this voyage as a private yacht had to be obtained from the Royal Navy as all recreational sailing in the Clyde and elsewhere was prohibited on the outbreak of the war.

Security was addressed. Under the 1911 Official Secrets Act the site was designated a 'prohibited place' and subject to all the restrictions imposed by that legislation. A strong barbed-wire fence was placed around the north, east and south boundaries of the yard while on the west or sea side new fences extended seawards from the yard to beyond the low tide line on both the north and south sides. Going into this area by any means was absolutely forbidden – no more were the Fairlie folk allowed to paddle, swim, fish, walk or use a boat on this part of their shore or sea. As the local paper reported, 'only the swans defy these orders and continue to sail around unhindered'. Entry to the yard itself was controlled via a gatehouse in Bay Street. No one without a special pass was allowed through. All of the security was enforced by a small team of Admiralty policemen and a special Establishment unit of the recently formed Fairlie Home Guard.

As elsewhere around the British coast, the extensive area of inter-tidal sands stretching south from Fairlie to Hunterston was seen as a location where the Germans might land by glider or parachute either to destroy the Establishment or steal its secrets. To prevent this possibility, stout wooden posts were driven into the sands as far out as the low-water mark. These were connected by a criss-cross grid of strong wires able to wreck any glider. The timber was obtained by

An aerial photograph of the site of the Establishment believed to have been taken shortly after the end of the Second World War. Other than the large shed on the left, next to the villa Dunora, all of the boatyard buildings shown are those requisitioned or constructed by the Admiralty. The iron-roofed building outwith the site at the corner of Bay Street and Pier Road, mid distance, accommodated the canteen. By the time of the photograph the wartime security fencing across the shore at the north and south ends of the site had been removed.

felling local woods, including an extensive area of pine trees growing where the present Fairlie Primary School exists, and just to the north of where William Fife (III) had built his large house, The Place, in 1907.

To protect against any U-boat intrusion into the Largs Channel it is believed that a hydrophone array was laid on the seabed from just south of Keppel Pier on Cumbrae across to the sands at Hunterston. This passive listening system is likely to have been monitored from a building near the pier and is said to have been linked to mines which could be detonated remotely from the Cumbrae shore. There is a reference to mines being disposed of when the hydrophone array was deactivated in 1946, and local people recall the occasional mine being washed ashore for some years after the war ended. The Keppel hydrophone array would have complemented a similar one placed across the main Clyde shipping channel between Cumbrae and Bute. This was monitored from another listening post on the north-west side of Cumbrae, the still existing buildings there being referred to locally as the 'Hush Hush'. In addition to these acoustic defences, physical steel net barriers were placed across the main Clyde channel between the Cloch Lighthouse and Dunoon, and across the much narrower channel between the Isle of Bute and Cowal at Colintraive. The net barriers, referred to as booms, had gates which could be opened and closed as ships required to pass through. It was hoped the hydrophone barriers would give advance warning of any U-boat that might try to slip through the gate when opened to allow a surface ship in or out.

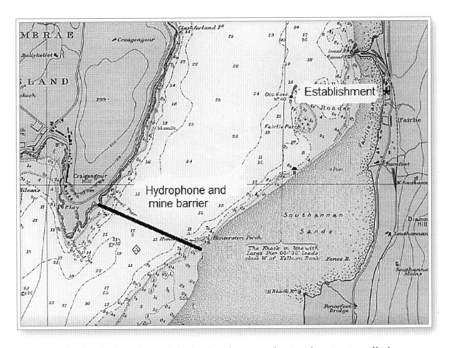

The likely location of the hydrophone and mine barrier installed to prevent U-boats entering the Largs Channel.

The installation of the hydrophone-controlled mine barrier between the south end of Cumbrae and Hunterston resulted in the Clyde steamer services from Fairlie to Millport, Arran and Campbeltown having to sail round the north end of the island. This restriction added considerably to the passage time of these essential passenger and cargo routes, particularly to that between Fairlie and Millport. All the ships that came to serve the Establishment also had to sail to and from Fairlie by the northerly route.

'What is going on' was of course a matter of much speculation among local people. Despite the great secrecy, it was soon common knowledge that the 'invaders' had come from Portland, that they worked for the Admiralty, and that their activities were somehow related to sinking German U-boats. But that was as much as anyone would learn for many years. Local people were advised in no uncertain terms that the work was highly secret and that on no account should they tell friends or family beyond the village anything about what they might see or

Widely distributed official notices ensured that Fairlie's residents were made aware of the highly secret nature of the Establishment's work, and the need to be very careful of the possibility of German spies.

The only known photograph of HM Anti-Submarine Experimental
Establishment Fairlie when it was in operation. It is believed to have been
taken by one of the senior scientific staff and was included in a paper
published in the first issue of the *Journal of the Royal Naval Scientific Service* –
a publication which was kept secret until 1972.

hear. Clearly explained were the consequences of 'loose talk' in relation
to the war effort. Also fully explained were the quite draconian regulations and penalties available to the authorities under the Defence of
the Realm Act and other wartime emergency legislation. Photography
anywhere without a permit was of course prohibited, again with severe
penalties for anyone found in breach of the regulations. Random visits
to Fairlie would be made by undercover Admiralty security officers to
check that the regulations were being observed.

Those working at the Establishment were also well warned of the
need for the utmost secrecy, and all the civilian employees had to sign
the Official Secrets Act. To minimise the risk of information getting
out, only a very few of the senior Establishment staff had an overall view
of the research being carried out. Those undertaking a specific project
had no knowledge of what project their colleagues might be involved
with. This 'need to know' security policy was similar to that imposed

at other wartime research establishments such as the code-breaking Bletchley Park.

The very high level of secrecy surrounding the Establishment was essential during the Second World War, and there is no evidence in the records that there were any serious security breaches during its time at Fairlie. Such was the importance of the research into how to locate a submerged submarine that for thirty years after the war's end the Establishment's records were locked away in the National Archives. All of this secrecy presented difficulties for those trying to find out about the Establishment and its work eighty years later.

Chapter 3

RESEARCH AND EXPERIMENTS: LOCATING U-BOATS

'The asdics did not conquer the U-boat; but without the asdics the U-boat would not have been conquered'

The existence of HM Anti-Submarine Experimental Establishment Fairlie was announced in January 1941 by the circulation of Confidential Admiralty Fleet Order 236, titled 'Anti-Submarine Branch and Establishments – Reorganisation'. The Order decreed that the purpose of HM Anti-Submarine Experimental Establishment Fairlie was 'to undertake research, experiments, development and design'. In effect the Establishment was charged with continuing the work interrupted at Portland by the German bombing and to expand and accelerate that work to counter the increasing U-boat attacks on shipping. By the end of 1940 the rate at which British merchant ships were being sunk was causing great alarm, and as in 1917 was threatening the country's imports of food and raw materials and its ability to continue to fight the war. Such was the concern about the escalating losses of ships and their vital cargoes that, after the war was over and Germany was defeated, Churchill was to confess that 'the only thing that ever really frightened me was the U-boat peril'.

Two main challenges were faced by those who had to defeat the Second World War U-boats: how to find them and then how to destroy or 'kill' them. As with all submarines, a U-boat could fire its torpedoes either when surfaced or when submerged. Once underwater

During a period of just seven days in September 1940, U-boats
repeatedly attacked a convoy crossing the Atlantic from Canada and
sank twenty-seven ships of nearly 160,000 tons. In the following month
a total of sixty-three ships were sunk, including the Clydebank-built
passenger liner *Empress of Britain*, and by the end of the year, some 471
ships of nearly 2.2 million tons had been lost to U-boat attacks. Most of
the losses occurred off the west coast of Ireland and most were the result
of night attacks by surfaced U-boats. This painting of a Second World
War U-boat is by the German marine artist Adolf Bock.

the submarine was powered by electric motors driven by batteries,
but the size and capacity of the batteries available throughout most
of the Second World War meant that both the underwater speed and
the duration of submergence were limited. When the power ran out,
the submarine had to surface and then run its diesel engines to recharge
the batteries. The diesel engines were also used to drive the submarine when sailing on the surface. With the two most common types
of Second World War U-boat the maximum surface speed was about

17 knots, but when submerged the speed was reduced to no more than around 7 knots.

This considerable disparity in speed meant that the U-boats generally travelled on the surface to reach their operational area and also more locally to locate the target and get into the best position for an attack. In the early years of the Second World War this was a relatively safe procedure, particularly at night, but as the war progressed the introduction of radar to both Royal Navy warships and Royal Air Force planes meant that surface movement became hazardous. The risk to the surfaced submarine was further increased when aircraft were able to attack as well as find the enemy. Thus the U-boats had to spend a greater proportion of their patrol time underwater and undertake almost all of their attacks on ships while submerged. When no longer visible to a ship or aircraft on the surface, the only way the U-boat could then be found was by underwater acoustic techniques. It was the development of these, and in particular improved types of asdic, that was the main thrust of the research and experimental work of the Establishment during its years in Fairlie. Supporting that activity was the introduction and testing of new means of sinking the submerged submarine.

The prewar development of asdic has been outlined in an earlier chapter. Here the much more rapid developments after 1940 will be described, but again not in every detail. Underwater acoustics is not an easy subject to understand. For any reader who might wish a much more scientific and comprehensive explanation of the role of acoustics in underwater warfare, the writer would suggest Willem Hackmann's book *Seek & Strike* which was published by Her Majesty's Stationery Office in 1984. An extremely detailed work, it was written with the assistance of two full-time researchers and many visits to the National Archives at Kew to peruse the Admiralty records. Because of the highly secret nature of the Establishment's work and its value to a potential postwar enemy, these official records remained classified until 1975, and it is likely that Hackmann was the first member of the public to gain access to them. But two caveats about *Seek & Strike*: first, the book is a government publication and therefore we must assume its content is likely to have been reviewed with regard to releasing into the public domain any still-sensitive material. And second, while the reader may not need to have a degree in acoustics to enjoy the book, some above-average knowledge of physics is very helpful. There are of course many other publications on all aspects of anti-submarine warfare for those wishing further reading, and a selection is listed at the end of the book.

Throughout the Second World War the hunting to destruction of a submerged U-boat was the most frequent aggressive role of the Royal Navy, and how to develop the tools to do this effectively was the responsibility of the supporting Admiralty scientists. As mentioned earlier, the scientists who moved from Portland to Fairlie at the end of 1940 included those who were acknowledged world leaders in the understanding and use of underwater acoustics. Indeed by the out-break of the war, some twenty-two different types of asdic had already been developed by the Portland HMS *Osprey* staff, including the main attack sets then in use by the Navy's destroyers, frigates and other sur-face warships. The relocated Establishment was not therefore starting from scratch but rather taking forward the work of the former Portland scientists, ably supported by the many very bright men and women who later came to join them at Fairlie.

As a simple and hopefully understandable explanation, a basic Second World War asdic set first and foremost comprised what was called a transducer. At the transducer's heart was a disc 15 inches in diameter made up of thin layers of quartz crystal sandwiched between layers of thin steel. The application of a high-voltage alternating cur-rent to the disc resulted in the quartz expanding and contracting at a very rapid frequency at regular intervals of a few seconds to produce a series of pressure waves in the surrounding water. A steel casing then directed the waves to produce a cone of supersonic sound extending outwards through the water in a manner similar to a searchlight beam. If the beam was intercepted by some object, the sound was reflected back to and received by the transducer. By noting the time between the transmitted sound and the receipt of any returned echo, and with some understanding of the speed of the sound through the water at the location, an indication was obtained of the distance of the reflecting surface from the transducer. Unlike the hydrophone, therefore, the transducer both transmitted pulses of acoustic energy as sound – the 'ping' noises heard in submarine films like the classic *Das Boot* (1981) and *The Hunt for Red October* (1990) – and also received as an echo that part of the energy returned from a reflecting surface. It was this ability of the transducer to both transmit and receive underwater sound that transformed the passive role of the hydrophone into the active underwater search tool, asdic.

To provide protection when the ship in which it was fitted was moving, the transducer was housed in a dome located at the bottom of the ship and projecting below the keel. In the early installations and in the smaller warships the projecting dome was fixed in place, but in the larger and faster warships such as the new destroyers and frigates it could be retracted into a special chamber or trunk within the hull to avoid damage at high speed and in bad weather. By rotating the transducer within the dome in a series of sideways steps and listening to the variation in the strength of the ping, a reasonable indication could be obtained of the bearing, or direction, of the echo. The pitch of the echo indicated whether the target was moving towards or away from the transducer.

The return signal or echo was relayed as an amplified sound to a small cabin on or very close to the bridge of the warship – usually referred to by the crew as the 'asdic hut'. Seated in the hut were one or more highly skilled specialist seamen operators. These operators were rated by the Royal Navy as Submarine Detectors 'SDs' and Higher Submarine Detectors 'HSDs' but were somewhat derisorily known by other rates as 'pingers'. They were trained during the Second World War first in the theory of underwater acoustics at HMS *Osprey* in Dunoon and then in practice at HMS *Nimrod* in Campbeltown. By 1945 the Navy had some 7,600 such ratings in its service.

The asdic operators were supervised by one of the warship's officers designated as the Anti-Submarine Control Officer, or ASCO. Most of the Second World War ASCOs were reservists and as such had received nothing like the level of training given at the specialist asdic courses held at Portland prior to 1939 for the career Royal Navy officers. Instead they had been rapidly passed through the much shorter wartime courses run at Dunoon and Campbeltown, followed by two to three weeks of very intensive instruction and testing on their ship as it 'worked up' at HMS *Western Isles*, the anti-submarine training base located at Tobermory on the Isle of Mull.

It was the role of the duty asdic set operator to direct the emitted sound as required, depending upon whether the asdic was being used to search for new contacts or to assist with the attack on an existing contact. The former, typically when escorting a convoy of merchant ships, involved repeated sweeps of the asdic beam in an arc forward of the escorting warship and could mean a whole watch passing without receiving any echo or return ping. But it was a duty that required the greatest concentration as failure to detect a U-boat lying at periscope

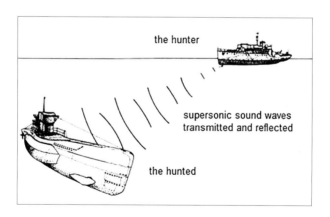

Supersonic sound waves transmitted from the warship's transducer and then reflected from the submerged submarine back to the transducer were the basis of asdic. The maximum detection range of an echo was about 7,500 feet, but during Second World War U-boat hunts, the average initial ping distance was about one third of that.

40

Arm badges of the Higher Submarine Detector (left) and Submarine Detector (right) ratings. The badges were initiated by the Royal Navy in 1930 and appropriately represent a coil of rope attached to a harpoon crossed by a streak of lightning. Because of the secrecy surrounding asdic, during the Second World War the 'pingers' were not allowed to wear these badges on their uniform so as to avoid any interest from enemy agents or special interrogation if taken prisoner.

depth just ahead of the approaching convoy could result in ships being sunk and vital cargoes lost. An asdic search by a convoy-escorting warship was an activity likened by one Royal Navy captain to 'looking in a dark room for a black cat that may or may not be there'.

When an echo was picked up, the ASCO and a second SD or the HSD were summoned to the asdic hut and the asdic operator through his skill and experience would advise if it was likely to be from a U-boat or from, for example, a wreck, a shoal of fish, or even a noisy whale, and whether the noise was approaching or moving away. Such judgement was very much based on the operator having an appreciation of the quality and characteristics of the noise received as the return echo, so much so that if an asdic rating was found to be really good at this interpretation, his commanding officer would do everything in his power to ensure that the rating remained with him if he was promoted to another command. As put by one of the training officers at Campbeltown, 'a good asdic operator is born, not bred'.

Once a contact had been agreed by the ASCO as a probable U-boat and the warship's commanding officer so advised, the concentration in the asdic hut became intense. Maintaining contact could lead to the destruction of the U-boat and the asdic team was required to use all

41

Concentration inside the asdic hut. A
submarine detector rating with a supervising
ASCO. Headphones assisted in hearing and
understanding the incoming echoes. The
officer has the sleeve insignia of a Lieutenant,
Royal Naval Volunteer Reserve (RNVR).

its skill and experience to keep track of the direction from where the
echo came – the bearing – and the distance from the transducer, at
first calculated using just a stopwatch to measure the time between the
transmitted and returned ping. Each change in bearing and distance
was reported to the warship's captain who would then endeavour to
take his ship close enough to the assumed U-boat to enable an effective
kill. But if the echo was lost, had the U-boat been sunk, or had it
evaded its hunters to attack later? The hunt for the black cat which
might or might not be in the dark room had to start all over again.

At the beginning of the Second World War the Royal Navy had three
standard asdic sets – one for relatively slow-moving convoy escort vessels, one for the faster U-boat hunting destroyers, and one for its own
submarines. All of these sets had been developed at Portland and were
in general use by 1937. Despite the best efforts of the Portland scientists, however, these prewar asdics were very limited in what they could

reveal about a U-boat's location, particularly with regard to how that changed relative to the hunter, and most importantly, at what depth below the surface it was. With the U-boat threat growing, the first task at Fairlie was to improve the existing sets, and in 1942 what was known as the Type 144 asdic was developed (all asdic developments were given a type number for ready identification). Its principal innovation was the electrochemical bearing recorder, which provided the operator with an image of the direction of each echo from the transducer as well as a record of how the bearing was changing. Worked in conjunction with an improved range recorder, this development greatly increased the ability of the attacking warship to follow the submerged U-boat and get into a position to fire its weapons. In effect the new range and bearing recorders gave asdic a memory. Both recorders had repeaters on the warship's bridge to assist the commanding officer in directing the attack.

A submarine can of course move in a third dimension by changing its depth below the sea surface. Thus the major problem which needed to be solved by the Fairlie scientists during the Second World War was how to determine the water depth from where the echo originated. The larger wartime U-boats were capable of descending to water depths of up to 750 feet – and sometimes more – and if they were to be sunk by some explosive device which detonated at a pre-set water depth, it was essential to know that depth. As the anti-submarine war moved from the relatively shallow waters of the British coast and the North Sea to the much deeper waters of the Atlantic Ocean, it thus became imperative to find a way of determining how far below the sea surface the submerged U-boat might be. This was particularly important when it became clear that, after an initial attack, U-boats were rapidly diving to water depths much greater than assessed at first discovery, and so evading the next attack by their hunters.

This problem was addressed as one of the highest priority by the Establishment's scientists. The first solution developed was to bring a vertical dimension to the acoustic signal by adding a second transducer within the asdic dome. This produced a very narrow beam, but one

HMS *Hadleigh Castle* was the first Royal Navy warship to be fitted with
a depth-determining type of asdic. Between North Atlantic convoy
escorting in January 1944 she demonstrated the new asdic to the United
States Navy. She is seen here about to anchor in the Clyde. Forty-four
Castle-class corvettes were built for the Royal Navy during the Second
World War, of which fourteen came from Clyde shipyards.

which could be angled downwards from the main beam by between 10
and 60 degrees to reach a depth of up to 700 feet. This was referred to
as the Q attachment and was first tested at Fairlie in February 1943.
The first operational unit was fitted to the new anti-submarine corvette
HMS *Hadleigh Castle* seven months later. Added to the Type 144 asdic
it was most effective when the U-boat was quite close, as in the lead up
to a depth-charge attack.

Being advised by the asdic operator where a submarine might be at
any moment in time is of limited help to those on a destroyer or frigate
trying to sink the submarine when both vessels are underway. What is
essential is to be aware of how the submarine is moving relative to the
hunter both horizontally and vertically. This required the position of
both the U-boat and the attacking warship to be recorded and then

continuously displayed as both travelled through the water. By closely watching the relative movements, including now any change in the depth of the U-boat, the warship's commanding officer could assess not only when to fire his weapons but as importantly at what depth they should be set to explode. The scientists working at Fairlie thus developed a plotting table on which the varying positions of hunter and hunted were continuously updated as determined by the range, depth and bearing recorders. Added to the data were the compass bearings of both the ship and the asdic transducer. 'All' the ship's captain then had to do was to watch the changing plot, order the coxswain to 'steer by asdic' to the U-boat's location, and then release his weaponry at the time computed by the plot. But this was much easier said than done, even for the most experienced captain of an anti-submarine destroyer or frigate.

In parallel with the development of the Q attachment for the Type 144 asdic, Fairlie produced a much more sophisticated version of asdic designated Type 147. This involved the design of a fan-shaped beam which was only 3 degrees wide in the vertical plane but 65 degrees wide in the horizontal plane, and able to be depressed up to 45 degrees from the horizontal. The transducer was mounted in a separate sword-shaped dome fitted forward of the main one. A true three-dimensional assessment of a U-boat's location could thus for the first time be available to the attacking warship. With an appropriate correction factor based on the sea temperature, the Type 147 was found to be accurate to within 20 feet when tested in Fairlie Bay by the Establishment scientists. Using Royal Navy submarines as targets, successful sea trials then took place in the deeper waters of the Firth of Clyde and North Atlantic in May 1943.

From inception to prototype testing, the development of the Type 147 by the Establishment was undertaken in the record time of just four months. After final approval by the Navy the new sets went into mass production at the Admiralty's Underwater Weapons Material Establishment at Bath in Somerset, and thereafter were rolled out for fitting to the Navy's new and existing anti-submarine warships. On

18 February 1944 the River-class frigate HMS *Spey* achieved the first sinking of a U-boat using the Type 147 depth-determining asdic. To demonstrate the effectiveness of the new type she followed this by sinking a second U-boat the next day. Her crew were later complimented by the Admiralty 'on good seamanship, efficient use of asdics, and the highest standards of depth-charge drill'.

With the addition of the associated bearing, distance and depth recorders, the Type 147 was the most important outcome of the asdic work undertaken at Fairlie and became the most effective of all the devices used by the Royal Navy during the Second World War for finding and then tracking submerged U-boats. As Winston Churchill stated at the end of the war, 'the asdics did not conquer the U-boat; but without the asdics the U-boat would not have been conquered'.

While the Type 147, and the modified Type 147B, were the last of the ship-borne asdics developed at Fairlie to be used in action in the Second World War, research and experimentation continued with versions which only came into their own after the war had ended. Among these Fairlie-initiated types was a very sophisticated split-beam technique, introduced to the Royal Navy in 1951 as Type 170, and an all-round electronically controlled scanning system known as Type 177. Also under development at the Establishment was a streamlined dome large enough to contain a range of both active and passive acoustic sensors. This dome was fitted to the Navy's postwar high-speed anti-submarine frigates.

In addition to offshore testing, extensive use was made of two former merchant ships which were moored in Fairlie Bay as floating, but static, acoustic laboratories. Further testing under moving conditions was then arranged by fitting the prototype devices to a Royal Navy warship. The main one used for these trials was the sloop HMS *Kingfisher* which transferred to Fairlie from Portland at the end of 1940 and remained part of the Establishment throughout the war. This ship worked with Royal Navy Clyde-based submarines which were tasked with simulating a U-boat. A second warship attached to the Establishment was a much smaller vessel that was used to test the shallow-water versions of asdic, which became necessary when the U-boats moved back from the Atlantic to waters closer to British shores. Fuller information about all of the ships that supported the Establishment is in a later chapter.

In its basic principle of operation, a U-boat-hunting asdic was very similar to the echosounders which are such a familiar feature today on most recreational yachts and motor boats, as well as on larger commercial vessels. Indeed the echosounder, or depth-measuring form of asdic, was one of the many different types of asdic prototypes developed at Fairlie. Just switch one on today and up comes the depth below the transducer either in digital or picture form. What most of us are not aware of when looking at the depth indicated by an echosounder, however, is that it is determined by the speed of sound through water, and that this speed is not constant because the acoustic characteristics of water are not constant.

The velocity at which a wave of supersonic acoustic energy passes through sea water varies with temperature, salinity, suspended solids, turbulence, pressure and other physical, chemical and even biological properties. And these properties continually vary with time, with location, and with water depth. The variation is not of any great importance with a small boat navigational echosounder, but knowing how it affects the speed of the sound signal and thus the distance of the echo from the transducer is essential if you are trying to locate a submarine submerged many hundreds of feet below the surface. Temperature is the most important variable. If the water temperature changes with depth, for example, the transmission speed of the asdic signal is in effect bent and the distance and bearing of the reflected object are no longer true. This problem became particularly noticeable with the Royal Navy warships escorting the convoys to Russia between October 1943 and May 1945. The layering of very cold Arctic water with warmer Gulf Stream surface water caused sharp negative drops in temperature at depths of 150 to 200 feet to the extent that one Murmansk convoy

The unseen enemy. The Type VIIC was the standard U-boat of the Second World War with a total of 568 being constructed. *U-995* is displayed at the Laboe Naval Memorial near Kiel. Note the large anti-aircraft armament which became necessary with increasing air attacks.

commander considered that a U-boat below these depths 'was almost impossible to detect by asdic'. Another, the senior officer of the escort for a returning convoy, vented his frustration by describing the use of asdic in these waters as 'trying to catch several irritated and offensively minded snakes with six harmless rabbits'.

Gaining understanding of the acoustic properties of the sea and how these vary was thus a major area of research for the Fairlie scientists. Throughout the Establishment's time in the village there was an oceanographer among the scientific staff. Extensive laboratory experiments and tests of hundreds of water samples using a special velocity meter contributed valuable information about how the transition layer between warmer water at the surface and colder water below (thermoclines) affect the acoustic signal. In October 1943 Fairlie's oceanographer sailed aboard one of the Russian convoy escort ships to take readings of the variation in temperature with depth using an American-designed instrument called a bathythermograph.

Awareness that the temperature, salinity and other properties of the sea are not uniform over the water depth was very important not only for those hunting a U-boat. It was also of great assistance to British submarines. In areas where thermoclines might be found, and the asdic distorted the submarine's depth, a submerged submarine could take advantage to reduce the chance of discovery. Like the U-boat captains, Royal Navy submarine commanders soon learned how to make use of thermocline waters. To help, both Royal Navy submarines and surface ships were soon fitted with recording thermometers. In the case of the Type 147B depth-determining asdic, the resulting knowledge of the temperature variation and its effect on the asdic signal was included in the calculation of the U-boat's probable location. Much of Fairlie's fundamental research on the relationship between sea temperature and sound propagation is still of critical value to both submariners and those who hunt submarines to this day.

And once the U-boat is found, how is it killed?

Chapter 4

RESEARCH AND EXPERIMENTS: KILLING U-BOATS

'a weapon with very great hitting power'

Having located and tracked a submerged U-boat through use of the new types of asdic, the next challenge for the Royal Navy was how best to attack and 'kill' the submarine both before and after it fired its torpedoes – possibly at the attacking warship. This was well described by one anti-submarine specialist as unlike any other form of warfare, being 'an attempt to sink an invisible enemy by a sense which is not in everyday use' – that sense being the interpretation of an underwater sound. Again the dark cat in the dark room – was that very slight noise made by the cat moving or by the door opening?

At the start of the Second World War the depth charge was the standard method of attacking a submerged U-boat. The depth charge was not a very sophisticated anti-submarine weapon – being in effect an underwater bomb – and by 1939 had not changed greatly in design and operation since the previous war. That most commonly used, designated the Mark VII, comprised a 28-inch-long by 18-inch-diameter steel cylinder filled with 290 lb (130 kg) of high explosive. The explosive was detonated by a pistol device actuated by the pressure of the water. This simple hydrostatic system allowed the depth charge to be set before release to explode at the depth where the U-boat was assumed to be. At first, depth charges were simply rolled over the stern of the attacking warship from rails, but to spread the potential kill area side throwers

Setting the firing pistols to the required depth in preparation for rolling depth charges off the stern of a Royal Navy warship. During repeated attacks this had to be done many times as the U-boat tried to escape.

were developed. Weights could be added to increase the depth charge's rate of sinking to minimise the time between release and explosion. The explosion depth could be set at between 100 and 500 feet, but both shallower and deeper settings became possible as the war progressed.

A Second World War depth charge did not need to impact a U-boat in order to sink it. When it exploded it produced a large gas bubble and it was the very fast cyclical expansion and contraction of this bubble which produced the shock waves which could cause severe or catastrophic damage to the submarine's pressure hull if the depth charge detonated within 20 feet or so. As more powerful explosives became available, this killing distance increased to about 50 feet. Tactical studies undertaken by the Establishment scientists in 1943 showed that, for stern release, a pattern of ten charges spaced at 180-foot intervals

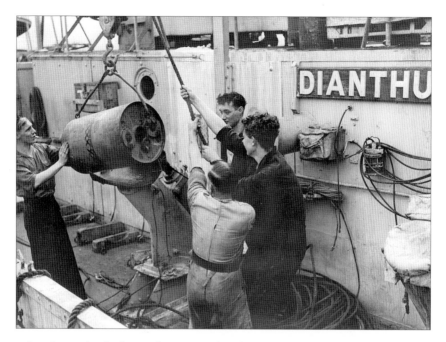

Loading a depth charge thrower on the Flower-class corvette HMS *Dianthus*. The Mark VII depth charge had a total weight of 420 lb (191 kg). Handling the charges required much physical effort by the warship's crew, especially with the ship heaving and rolling in heavy weather.

was a good balance between the probability of a kill and the number of depth charges dropped, once the U-boat's location had been determined with some certainty. The addition of side throwers to extend the targeted breadth further optimised the charges per salvo. These studies of course assumed the best use by the attacking warship of the latest types of asdic.

Depth charges were popular with the crews of anti-submarine vessels. Even if no damage was actually caused to the U-boat, the great skywards heave of water thrown up by the underwater explosion showed the warship's sailors that at least an attack was being made, and as such maintained morale. Again, even if the U-boat was not destroyed by a first salvo or had not experienced enough damage to cause it to abandon its patrol, its crew had to have the stamina and nerves to withstand the stress of further nearby explosions, especially if the attack was sustained over many hours, as some often were. Much more satisfying to the crew of an attacking warship, of course, was evidence of the U-boat having been sunk through oil and debris appearing on the sea surface, or the depth charge damage being sufficient to force the submarine to the surface where it could be attacked and sunk by the warship's guns, or in some cases just rammed.

Depth charges exploding astern of the attacking warship. Because of the shock force of the underwater explosion, it was vital that the warship moved quickly away from the release point to avoid damage to itself. River-class frigates such as the previously mentioned HMS *Spey* could carry some 150 depth charges and during a prolonged attack on a U-boat it was not unusual for all of the supply to be expended.

The depth charge had significant limitations when used with the early forms of asdic. The first problem was that the underwater turbulence and aeration created by its detonation rendered the asdic signal ineffective until the distortion of the water column ceased. A further attack had to either wait until the water disturbance settled, or be attempted with no strong asdic signal. This delay could be used by the still active U-boat to move away from its attacker.

A second limitation arose from the relative movement of the warship and the submerged U-boat after the first asdic contact. While the warship was initially able to keep sailing towards the location of the echo, the cone shape of the forward-pointing asdic beam generally meant that contact was lost as the distance ahead reduced to around 700 feet. The warship thus had to continue over that distance for a minute or so acoustically blind until the U-boat's last known position was reached and the depth charges released. U-boat captains also became aware of this delay and if they rapidly changed direction after the ping of the asdic signal they were hearing reduced or ceased, then they could with some luck get safely distanced from the likely position of the expected next depth charge attack.

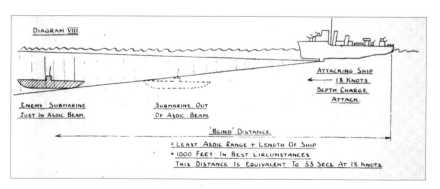

The blind area of asdic when attacking with depth charges. As the warship moves left towards the U-boat the transmitted sound cone passes beyond the submarine's location and the contact is lost. When the depth charges are released at the last noted position or depth, the U-boat may no longer be there.

The answer to these difficulties was to develop a device which could fire a depth charge, or some similar type of underwater bomb, forwards over the bow of the attacking warship while a strong asdic contact still existed. The development and use of these ahead-throwing weapons are described in some detail in *Seek & Strike* and other anti-submarine histories. The following highlights only those aspects of these new weapons relating to the role of the Establishment at Fairlie.

The concept of a weapon able to fire an anti-submarine projectile or 'bomb' forward of a warship was first developed by the Royal Navy during the First World War when some Army howitzers were adapted for fitting to a few small warships. However, interest in the concept ceased at the end of the war and it was not until the improved types of asdic became available that the potential of such a weapon was fully appreciated by the Admiralty and development accelerated. The scientists of HMS *Osprey* were among those given the task of developing an effective forward-throwing anti-submarine weapon. Under the leadership of Benjamin Smith, a former Shandon and Portland scientist now in charge at Fairlie, a design was quickly produced for a device which could be mounted at the forward end of a warship. From this position a

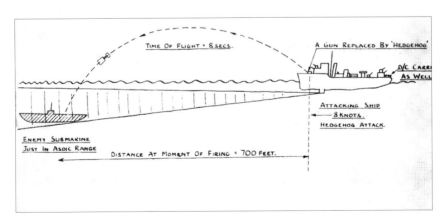

Throwing a weapon ahead of the warship enabled the U-boat to be attacked while asdic contact was maintained. Knowing the trajectory of the projectile and when to fire it was then critical to success.

projectile could be fired over the bow and well out in front of the moving ship. Appropriately, this early device was known as the Fairlie Mortar.

No photograph of the Fairlie Mortar has been found, but it is described as comprising two sets of ten mortar barrels each firing a projectile containing 20 lb (9 kg) of high explosive. The timing of each firing was so arranged as to form a circular pattern around the U-boat's last position on entering the sea. To increase the rate of sinking, a heavy lead weight was included in the nose of each projectile. Unlike the depth charge, which could be set to explode at a specified depth, the much lighter and less powerful mortar projectiles were designed to detonate only on impacting the hull of a U-boat. This caused difficulties. Sea trials of a Fairlie Mortar mounted on the Establishment's trials warship HMS *Kingfisher* revealed that a fuse strong enough to withstand impact with the sea surface did not detonate when hitting the submerged submarine's relatively weak outer casing. It was also suggested that the quantity of explosive in each projectile – about 7 per cent of that in a depth charge – was not sufficient to hole a U-boat's pressure hull even with a direct hit and detonation on the outer casing.

The Fairlie Mortar was only one of a number of ahead-throwing devices under development. In August 1941, despite the strong opposition of Smith and the other Establishment scientists, the Admiralty decided to abandon the mortar concept and proceed instead with a device which could project a salvo of twenty-four small bombs forwards after being fired electrically from spigots instead of barrels. The quill-like appearance of the multiple spigots – basically steel pegs – on which the projectiles were mounted resulted, naturally, in the system being given the name Hedgehog. Again, unlike the depth charge, which exploded at a pre-set depth, the much smaller and less powerful Hedgehog bombs exploded only if they actually hit the submarine. If they did not, they simply sank to the bottom.

This was found to have two disadvantages. For the attacking warship it meant that there was no longer the upward heave of water to give some satisfaction to those firing the weapon, while the absence

The twenty-four projectiles of Hedgehog were fired in pairs at 1.5 second intervals and, on hitting the sea, would form a circle about 100 feet in diameter. Hedgehog was developed by the Admiralty's Department of Miscellaneous Weapons Development (DMWD), a group that comprised a mix of young scientists and older military officers. The members were generally referred to as the 'wheezers and dodgers' and were responsible for introducing many innovative new weapons in the Second World War.

of any explosion removed the psychological impact on the U-boat's crew of the noise and shaking of repeated near misses from a sustained depth-charge attack. Thus what the Royal Navy sailors referred to as the 'new-fangled weapon' was not popular, with one destroyer captain going so far as to describe it as 'bloody useless'. These difficulties, which after investigation were found to be mainly the result of poor crew training, in turn caused a lack of enthusiasm for its use in preference to the more powerful and spectacular depth charges. On the other hand, the absence of an explosion and resulting water turbulence allowed the warship, or increasingly a pair of such ships, to continue the asdic-guided attack with a second Hedgehog salvo as soon as the spigots could be reloaded by the crew. The accuracy and effectiveness of Hedgehog was greatly improved when firing was controlled by the Type 144 asdic with the Q attachment, as intended by Smith. Once sufficient operational experience had been gained by the warship crews, Hedgehog did become an effective anti-submarine weapon, accounting for some forty-eight U-boat kills by the end of the war.

The relatively small explosive charge of each Hedgehog projectile of 30 lb (13.5 kg) and the consequential need for a direct hit to be effective caused the Admiralty to revisit the Fairlie Mortar with its barrel firing. In early 1942, trials were undertaken with a larger version containing more explosive known – for reasons only those in the Admiralty would comprehend – as Parsnip. While the Parsnip design was again not taken further, the trials soon led to what was to become the most important of all the Royal Navy anti-submarine weapons developed during the Second World War. Given the name Squid, this next forward-throwing weapon consisted of a triple 12-inch-diameter barrel mortar-type mounting, able to fire projectiles containing some 200 lb (90 kg) of explosive for a distance of up to 1,000 feet in front of the attacking warship. It returned to the depth charge concept of firing an explosive charge which detonated at a pre-set depth rather than by direct contact, with the three projectiles of each salvo being aimed to form a tight triangle around the target's location. Fitting the attacking warship with a pair of the triple barrel mountings further increased the chance of a direct hit. Squid was effective down to a depth of 900 feet, thus able to reach the deepest diving U-boats of the Second World War.

The first Squid was mounted on a Royal Navy warship in August 1943 after trials at Fairlie (described later), but it was not until the end of July 1944 that the new weapon, fired from the Burntisland-built Loch-class anti-submarine frigate HMS *Loch Killin*, sank its first U-boat. While Benjamin Smith was by then long gone from Fairlie, it must have given him considerable satisfaction to see his mortar concept fully vindicated – even if Squid was considered a more acceptable name to the Admiralty than Fairlie Mortar.

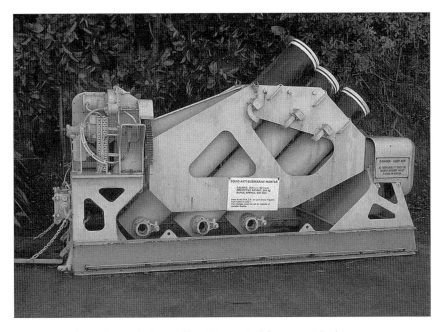

A single triple-barrel Squid intended for use with the new
Loch-class anti-submarine frigates.

As with Hedgehog, the key to effective use of Squid in attacking a
submerged U-boat was the prediction of the time of firing the projectiles and the setting of the detonation depth. Both were determined
from the Type 147B asdic equipment with its recording of the U-boat's
position and depth. Thereafter the critical linkage between asdic and
detonation was developed at Fairlie by the Establishment scientists
through what would today be termed the system software. Using the
relative positions of the attacker and attacked and how this changed
as the attack progressed, this computed the optimum moment for
Squid to be fired, and thereafter automatically initiated setting of the
explosion depth and then firing of the projectiles. The result was the
first fully integrated submarine attack system, one which successfully
combined identification of the U-boat's location with attack by powerful forward-throwing projectiles. Described by one frigate captain
as 'a weapon with very great hitting power', the combination of Squid

The destroyer HMS *Barrosa* sailing through the effect of
Squid explosions during postwar trials.

and the Type 147B asdic was a winner. Royal Navy analysis after the
war showed that the chance of a submerged U-boat being sunk by
a Squid attack was roughly 50 per cent as against 20 per cent for
one using Hedgehog and just 6 per cent for a depth-charge attack.
A further development of Squid under the name Limbo became the
Royal Navy's standard anti-submarine weapon through the 1950s and
early 1960s.

The Fairlie scientists also undertook the practical experiments that
were an essential precursor to the new system's success. As mentioned
earlier, a depth charge was quite a simple weapon and one of its sim-
plicities was that it sank and then detonated very close to where it was
released – hence the need for the dropping warship to move quickly
away from that point. But forward-throwing weapons like Hedgehog
and Squid were very different. Their explosive charges were projectiles
which flew through the air before entering the water at some distance

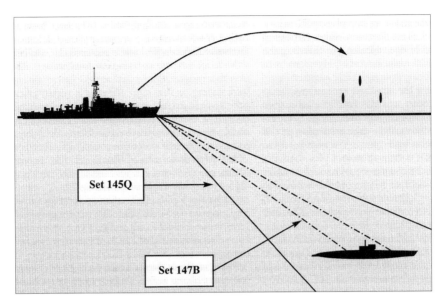

The Royal Navy's ultimate Second World War weapon system for finding
and sinking the U-boat was the depth-determining Type 145 asdic with the
Q attachment, followed by the Type 147B asdic, and the linking of these to
the forward-throwing Squid to determine the time of firing and the depth
setting – all work done at Fairlie. Once a U-boat had been detected, its chance
of avoiding destruction was very slim. By the end of the Second World War the
new system was credited with destroying a total of seventeen U-boats.

ahead of the firing point. After firing, the projectiles followed a trajectory – initially rising upwards and then falling downwards as the
forward velocity reduced and gravity became the dominant driving
force. If all the forward velocity had ceased at the point where the
projectile entered the sea then the projectile would settle vertically
downwards at that point. But if there was still some forward velocity
remaining from the firing then that would continue to move the projectile forward through the water and away from the entry location.
What path below the water surface did the projectile follow until only
vertical movement took place and the U-boat's location was reached?

Providing answers to essential questions such as this was greatly
enhanced by use of what was known as the Fairlie Underwater Range.
This was set up in great secrecy during the summer of 1941. It comprised

six very sensitive hydrophones precisely located on the bed of the Largs Channel some three-quarters of a mile to the west of the Establishment in a water depth of about 145 feet. The hydrophones were linked by underwater cable to a shore recorder in one of the Establishment's laboratories from where an uninterrupted view of the range area was obtained for observations and signalling by the scientists undertaking the experiments. Before being fired from one of the trials ships, a projectile under test was fitted with a series of delay action electric detonators actuated in turn as the projectile moved through the water. By recording and analysing the sound emitted by the detonations and the signals received by each of the hydrophones (and some complicated trigonometry), an accurate representation was obtained of the projectile's underwater trajectory or path. Further information about where the projectile entered the water and its velocity and direction at this point relative to the firing point could also be found by comparing the time of firing and the time of striking the water surface. Putting the two together provided the time between firing of the projectile and when it should reach a known location and depth, and hopefully the U-boat.

The underwater range was also used to optimise the rate of sinking of both depth charges and ahead-throwing projectiles once in the water. It was essential that after entering the sea all of these weapons descended as quickly as possible to the asdic-determined depth. Thus refinements could be made to the weight and shape of the various depth charges, Hedgehog and Squid projectiles, using the test data from the range's hydrophones.

The underwater trajectory range at Fairlie was the only one of its kind in existence in Britain during the Second World War and was extensively used not just by warships testing the ahead-throwing weapons but also by the Coastal Command aircraft of the Royal Air Force. Depth charges dropped from planes like the Catalina, Sunderland and Liberator played an increasingly important role in sinking the U-boats and knowing the expected trajectory of these underwater bombs after release by the plane was vital to a successful attack. All of this activity

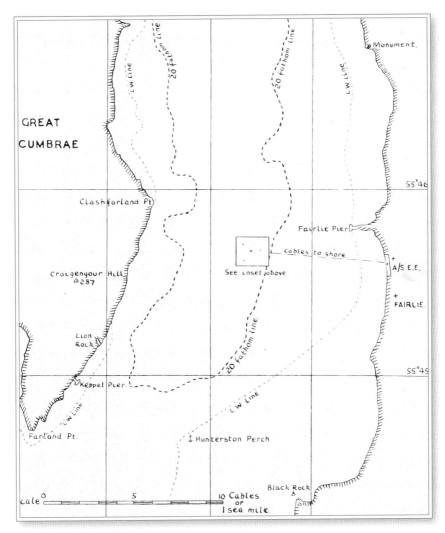

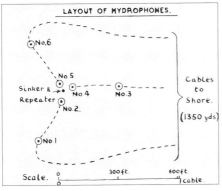

(*Top*) The location of the Fairlie Underwater Range in the Largs Channel, in a document headed 'SECRET'. (*Bottom*) Detail of the six hydrophone positions on the seabed.

in the nearby Largs Channel is said to have added 'considerable inter-est' for the Establishment's staff as they watched from their office and workshop windows – and presumably was also of considerable interest to any Fairlie folk who might also be watching from their windows or gardens. Unfortunately, no photographs of the many tests have been found in the National Archives and it would appear that never a word was spoken by any of the locals about what they might have seen . . .

Studies of the pre-entry trajectory of Squid projectiles and the actual spacing of where those fired in each salvo impacted were also under-taken at Fairlie. The extensive area of relatively flat beach between the high and low water marks of the Fairlie and Southannan Sands to the south of Bay Street allowed projectiles to be fired onto the sands at low tide and their landing points determined. This involved precise but quite standard land survey techniques to locate both the landing and firing points. In July 1944 the destroyer HMS *Ambuscade* undertook such firing to confirm the accuracy of Squid. While the test projectiles did not contain any explosive, the double Squid pattern of six projec-tiles at a time hurtling towards the Fairlie shore must have been, to say the least, of some concern to any local residents who might have had the courage to watch. But again, there are no photographs or recorded recollections.

While the main thrust of the Establishment's research and experi-mental work was always related to finding and sinking U-boats through

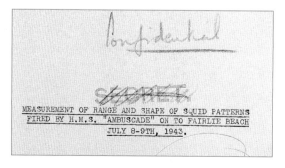

The Establishment's report on the Squid firing
onto the Fairlie beach.

HMS *Ambuscade* was used to test Squid by firing projectiles onto the
beach at Fairlie. The Squid launcher can be seen on the ship's foredeck,
where it replaced one of the guns.

the development of the Type 144 and Type 147 asdic sets, some twenty-
three other forms of asdic were developed at Fairlie. Royal Navy submarines faced the same difficulties and dangers as German ones during
the war and as such a considerable amount of work was undertaken
at the Establishment into the development of acoustic devices for use
by British submarines. These were of both active and passive forms
– the former to better detect and attack enemy vessels and to avoid
dangers ahead such as mines and wrecks. The passive forms of asdic,
more correctly sophisticated hydrophones, were developed to provide
early warning of the approach of enemy vessels without the submarine giving away its own presence to these vessels by transmitting. By
simply switching off the outgoing ping signal and just listening for
any noises received, a U-boat-hunting warship or submarine could get
good warning of the presence of such a boat – if it was making a noise
– without revealing its presence by transmitting.

Two submarines attempting to kill each other with only the hydrophone sensors giving any guidance to their respective locations required their captains to have great skill and strong nerves. Even today submariners engaged in this potentially deadly form of underwater hide and seek find the experience challenging. It has been likened by one Royal Navy captain to 'a duel between two persons with loaded guns searching in a totally dark room with only any very slight sound made by one helping the other to aim and fire their gun first'. As with other developments initiated at Fairlie, research into improving the sensitivity and range of the hydrophone as a passive submarine detector was to be given the highest priority in the years after the end of the Second World War.

In December 1941 the Italian Navy used what were in effect manned torpedoes to cause serious damage to Royal Navy battleships lying at Gibraltar and Alexandria. The attacks caused the Admiralty great concern as it was feared that the 'human torpedoes' would pose a threat to the many other harbours and anchorages used by warships and merchant vessels. Because the attackers moved at or just below the water surface, the seabed hydrophone arrays were not effective, so Fairlie was given the task of finding another way of detecting them. By early 1942 an updated version of a harbour defence asdic first developed at Portland in the 1930s was ready for use. This operated like a horizontal asdic and was soon installed at the ends of breakwaters, piers and other parts of a harbour, and also on the hulls of the most valuable warships.

The Royal Navy developed its own version of a small submersible in the form of a 'midget' submarine known as an X-craft. This very small and very secret submarine was a response to the extreme threat presented to North Atlantic and Russian convoys by the German battleship *Tirpitz*. Lying protected from air attack in a Norwegian fjord, but able to go to sea at any time, *Tirpitz* required the Navy to keep many of its own scarce battleships ready to react. She had to be put out of action.

Tirpitz on her mooring at Kåfjorden in the far north of Norway.
From this location she could easily strike at the Arctic convoys.

The plan was to use the X-craft to enter the fjord, make their way submerged to the battleship, and then place time-delayed explosive charges below her hull before retreating seaward. To do this, an asdic able to measure distance above the transducer was required, and again the task was given to the scientists at Fairlie. The resulting Type 151 asdic had a very narrow beam and was mounted on top of the submarine's casing. This enabled the X-craft's commander to determine when his boat with its explosive charges was directly under the target and the charges could be released for later detonation. To assist in passing below or through the anti-submarine nets protecting the battleship, a depth-determining asdic – the modern echosounder – was designed and installed. The X-craft attack on *Tirpitz* took place in September 1943 and succeeded in causing enough damage to reduce her immediate threat to the convoys. In July 1945 a similar operation sank the Japanese cruiser *Takao* moored off Singapore. X-craft were also used to sever some of the underwater telephone cables that the Japanese relied upon for inter-island communication.

During D-Day some of the X-craft were used to act as navigational beacons for the landing craft, a task which required Fairlie to develop yet another type of asdic. A further contribution of the Fairlie scientists

Based at Port Bannatyne on the Isle of Bute, the three- or four-man X-craft midget submarines used for the attack on *Tirpitz* trained in the secluded waters of nearby Loch Striven. All of the special types of asdic required for their operations were developed very quickly and in the greatest secrecy by the scientists at Fairlie.

to the success of the D-Day landings was the development of the asdic fitted to the larger landing craft to enable them to detect and avoid the many underwater obstructions which the Germans had placed on the most likely invasion beaches.

The main source of underwater noise of interest to the scientists of the Establishment was that made by the rotation of a ship's or submarine's propeller. This noise results from the phenomenon of cavitation. As water is accelerated by a turning propeller, its pressure falls and tiny air bubbles are formed by vaporisation. When the bubbles move outwards to the trailing edge of the propeller, the water pressure rises, causing them to suddenly implode. As the noise made by the implosions could easily be detected by the hydrophone of the submarine's hunter, it was important to reduce its cause and thus the risk of a

British submarine being detected by the Germans. Cavitation noise was studied in some detail at Fairlie by its hydrodynamic specialists both by using the water-filled propeller tank installed in one of the Bay Street buildings, and by hydrophone measurements at sea. Many different shapes of propeller blade were investigated in the test tank, as well as the number of blades in each propeller and the effect of the speed of rotation. Also tested were different surface coatings, and the injection of air bubbles around the propeller as a means of reducing the cavitation and thus the acoustic signal of the ship or submarine. Like much of the Establishment's Second World War research, the work on reducing propeller noise while maintaining the propeller's thrust continued long after the end of the war, and indeed still continues as shown by the multi-bladed slow-turning propeller of today's submarines.

A more immediate propeller noise problem given to the Fairlie scientists to solve was that caused by the introduction by the Germans of the acoustic torpedo, called GNAT by the Royal Navy, in September 1943. After being fired by a U-boat, this steered itself towards a moving ship by using an internal hydrophone device to home in on the ship's propeller noise. It then exploded on impact. GNAT was a troubling new weapon as it was particularly effective against the higher-propeller-speed, and thus noisier, warships escorting convoys. With its acoustic expertise, Fairlie was asked to come up with an effective countermeasure. This the scientists did in a matter of weeks by designing a mechanical device which created a greater noise profile than the propeller. Towed astern of the ship, the device was given the code name Foxer and, while cumbersome to deploy, it proved very effective. However, the noise also interfered with a warship's asdic to the extent that often the Foxer had detonated the GNAT before the firing U-boat had been detected. Because of these difficulties, Foxer was eventually replaced by a simpler and lighter device developed by the Royal Canadian Navy.

While the Admiralty had shown some interest before the Second World War in torpedoes that could be guided towards their target by sound, it was not until 1942 that the Establishment's scientists were asked to look in detail at the acoustics. Working with the Torpedo Experimental Establishment at Greenock a few miles further up the Clyde, Fairlie undertook extensive theoretical research as well as testing using the underwater range. But the high priority of the asdic work meant that the project was suspended and it was not until the Royal Air Force asked the scientists to assist with below-water acoustic steering of an air-launched torpedo that experiments resumed. As the war progressed, both guided and homing air-launched, ship-launched and submarine-launched torpedoes became increasingly important for anti-submarine and anti-ship attacks. Again, the Establishment provided expert advice on the acoustics and the use of the underwater range for testing. This new type of underwater weapon – particularly the submarine-launched anti-submarine homing torpedo as used by the 'hunter killer' submarines of today – was to become of great importance in the next decades.

As explained earlier, the U-boat's maximum underwater speed of around 7 knots and quite short submerged endurance, common to all submarines of the time, imposed a significant limitation on their survivability. Once the U-boat had been detected by asdic and was under attack when submerged, this speed made it difficult to outrun the faster destroyers and frigates engaged in the hunt. In the shallower coastal waters around Britain targeted by the U-boats from 1944, it thus became common that instead of trying to move away after an attack, the submarine opted to stay still and silent resting on the sea-bed. That seabed, particularly along the English Channel, was cluttered with old wrecks and other debris and the hope was that it would not be found by the hunter's asdic among the many different echoes. Fairlie gave considerable attention to this problem, but a way of separating out the size and shape of the features causing the echo was not finally solved until after the war was over. Until it was, the Royal Navy soon realised that the hunting warship just needed to have the patience to wait until the U-boat's air started to run out. After it was forced to surface, gunfire usually assured its destruction.

So how could a submarine stay longer and travel faster under water when discovery by underwater acoustics was at that time its only opponent? The first solution to the challenge of extending the submerged duration was developed by the Germans with the introduction of the schnorkel – the name now also given to the short tube which enables the human user to swim with head submerged. First used by the Dutch Navy before the Second World War, the schnorkel tube could be raised like the periscope above the sea surface while the submarine remained submerged. In this position it allowed enough air to be drawn into the submarine to run its diesel engines, with a secondary tube being provided to discharge the exhaust gas. Very successful, the fitting of a schnorkel meant that the U-boat could recharge its batteries without having to surface. Only the top of the schnorkel tube offered a visible or radar target, which greatly reduced the U-boats' increasing losses to air attack.

While underwater, a Second World War submarine could only move at the speed allowed by its electric motors. Two characteristics limit that underwater speed – the power of the propulsion system and the resistance to movement through the water resulting from the shape and smoothness of the submarine's external features. Higher-capacity batteries were one short-term solution to the power limitation, but if the below-water frictional resistance or drag could be reduced, a submarine could travel faster without any increase in propulsive power. This challenge was given much consideration by the German Navy and early in 1944 British intelligence discovered that work had started on a new design of U-boat with a high underwater speed. Known as the Type XXI, the design was believed to incorporate a very low hydrodynamic drag profile and much larger batteries, which in combination were intended to give a submerged sprint speed of at least 18 knots, and an underwater average speed of 10 knots sustainable for up to ten hours.

The possibility of a U-boat with an underwater speed of 18 knots or more was of great concern to the Admiralty as it would mean that, while submerged, the U-boat could outrun and evade many of the Royal Navy warships then in use for convoy protection. The ubiquitous

U-3008 was one of only two Type XXI high-speed U-boats completed in time to undertake a wartime patrol. After surrendering in the Baltic in May 1945 she was taken over by the United States Navy for extensive testing.

Flower-class corvettes, for example, could only manage a top speed of 16 knots, while there was no certainty that even the Loch-class frigates coming into service in 1944 would be fast enough. It was also feared that the current types of asdic would be less effective when required to function at such speeds because of the increased turbulence and other acoustic challenges.

To counter the potential threat it was necessary to have some knowledge of the acoustic properties of a submarine with a high underwater speed. As none of the Type XXI boats were yet in service, tests would have to be carried out with a British submarine. The Establishment was therefore asked to investigate how the submerged speed of one of the Royal Navy's existing submarines might be increased by streamlining its underwater profile. Stream lines are the representations of the path followed by a particle of fluid moving around an object – the air flow over an aeroplane wing for example. The Fairlie scientists had extensive experience of streamlining through their research into the optimum shape of the asdic domes fitted to all Royal Navy warships so as to minimise the effect of cavitation on the asdic signal.

HMS *Seraph* was the submarine chosen. She was one of the Royal Navy's S-class attack submarines and was built at Barrow-in Furness in 1942. *Seraph* is best known for the role she played in Operation Mincemeat, a plan intended to convince the Germans that the first Allied Mediterranean landings would take place in Greece and Sardinia and not in Sicily. The subterfuge involved the release into the sea off Spain of a body dressed in the uniform of an officer in the Royal Marines, attached to which was a briefcase containing 'highly secret' plans and other documents relating to the forthcoming invasion. The intention was that the floating corpse, meant to be from an air crash, would be found by the Spanish, who would most likely pass the secret information on to the Germans.

HMS *Seraph* was selected to deliver the body of the fictitious 'Major Martin' and on 17 April 1943 it was loaded in great secrecy aboard the submarine at Greenock in a metal canister. The submarine then sailed to the Spanish coast where, in the early hours of 30 April, the body (believed at the time to be of an unknown vagrant) was placed in the sea. As expected, it was found by a Spanish fisherman and, after some time, copies of the documents were on their way to Berlin. The Germans were duly deceived, with the result that the Sicily landings on 9 July were not as strongly opposed as they could have been, saving many lives. In 1953 the best-selling book *The Man Who Never Was* told the story of the deception, and three years later a film of the same title was released. In 2022 the story was told in the film *Operation Mincemeat*.

Following her key role in Operation Mincemeat and other secret missions, *Seraph* was undergoing major repairs in the summer of 1944. After inspection by the Fairlie scientists it was decided that she would be suitable for conversion as the required trial vessel. More powerful electric motors were fitted and, with the advice of the Establishment's specialists, her flow resistance was reduced by removing or reshaping all her external fittings, particularly the streamlining of the conning

HMS *Seraph* after streamlining. *Seraph* remained part of the
Royal Navy's submarine fleet until 1961 and appeared as herself in
the 1956 film *The Man Who Never Was*.

tower. This work was completed by the end of September 1944
with trials on the Clyde showing an underwater speed increase from
7 knots to 12 knots. Over the next few weeks *Seraph* worked with
the Establishment's trials ship HMS *Kingfisher* and other warships to
enable the Fairlie scientists to gain valuable practical data on how asdic
needed to be improved if contact was to be maintained between hunter
and hunted at higher speeds. The ability to change (in a rapid but
controlled way) the orientation of *Seraph*'s streamlined hull relative to
Kingfisher's asdic beam was particularly useful: it showed how variable
the asdic echo could be as the profile of the submarine altered relative
to the asdic beam. These urgent sea trials took place in the Firth of
Clyde and in the more exposed west-coast waters, sometimes, it was
reported, with not the best of effects on the stomachs of the participat-
ing Fairlie scientists.

The results of the trials and further exercises where HMS *Seraph* acted
as a training target for the Navy's anti-submarine groups were of some

concern to the Establishment. They showed how difficult it was for the current best types of asdic to keep track of a submarine able to change position in three dimensions at a greater speed than even the most experienced of the hunters could follow. The resulting Admiralty report of the trials concluded that 'as a high-speed submarine does not allow time to correct small errors in ship handling and operating, the very highest of training standards would be needed for any chance of success.' Most significantly, it was also acknowledged that a U-boat able to move submerged at 18 knots or more would require a step change not only in asdic development but also in all of the then current techniques of anti-submarine warfare.

The imminent introduction of the Type XXI high-speed U-boat was not the only concern of the Royal Navy in the closing months of the war. Also developed by the Germans was the Type XXIII. This was a quite small submarine intended for operations in shallow coastal waters and incorporated the streamlining and higher underwater speed of the larger Type XXI design. Introduced to operational service in January 1945, the Type XXIII U-boats concentrated their attacks on shipping moving along the east coast of Scotland. Here they sunk or damaged five small vessels. One of these was the British steamer *Avondale Park* which was torpedoed just after 11 pm on 7 May 1945, only an hour before the end of the Second World War. The attack took place near the Isle of May at the entrance to the Firth of Forth – by a strange coincidence within just a few miles of where HMS *Pathfinder* was torpedoed in the early days of the First World War.

It was not the sinking of the five ships which was of greatest concern to the Royal Navy but the knowledge that, despite the presence of a large number of escort vessels in the area, no asdic contacts had been obtained from any of the Type XXIII boats. The inability of asdic to find the new type of submarine caused the then First Sea Lord, Admiral Cunningham, to comment 'we are having a difficult time with these U-boats – the asdic is failing us in confined waters with strong tidal streams'.

75

Fortunately for Britain and her Allies, the Second World War ended before more than a handful of the new streamlined and very quiet Type XXI and Type XXIII U-boats became operational, and before the even more worrying Type XXVI boats fitted with an engine which did not require any external air supply could come into service. How to find and kill a submarine with an underwater speed of 20 knots and more, able to stay submerged for weeks at a time, and with a small acoustic profile, would be a serious challenge indeed for Britain's postwar anti-submarine forces. The trials and tests carried out at Fairlie in the closing months of the war indicated just how difficult it would be for the Royal Navy to meet that challenge.

Being a Royal Navy establishment, the emphasis of the work undertaken at Fairlie was always on the rapid provision of effective solutions to immediate problems. And throughout the Second World War the overriding problem to be addressed was how to locate and attack the submerged U-boat and protect the vital convoys. Thus the research and experiments carried out at the Establishment were primarily concerned with developing and improving the equipment needed to achieve that objective. Asdic to find the enemy submarine, the testing of ahead-throwing weapons to sink it, and the linkage of the two to ensure an accurate and effective underwater attack, were each critical to that task. And, just in time, the task was successfully completed. That is the Establishment's, and Fairlie's, wartime legacy.

Chapter 5

THE PEOPLE

*'a place they shipped scientists they
didn't know what to do with'*

The contribution of the Fairlie Establishment to the defeat of Germany represented the collective efforts of the many men and women who worked there from October 1940 until February 1946. These people came from a wide range of social backgrounds and from many different parts of the British Isles – and some from overseas. They each had their own skills, abilities and, in not a few cases, foibles. At times their different personalities meant that they did not always work together in perfect harmony and at times some were exasperated by what they saw as the intransigence of their colleagues. But throughout their service at Fairlie they researched, developed, built, tested, proved and delivered the asdic equipment without which the Royal Navy could not have achieved success in its battle with the U-boats.

Those employed at Fairlie during the Establishment's life can be divided into four broad groups by role and responsibility. First and foremost, HM Anti-Submarine Experimental Establishment Fairlie was a 'ship' of the Royal Navy. It may not have floated and it may not have been given an HMS name, but it most certainly was part of the Navy. As such, a naval officer was always in overall charge of its day-to-day activities. The senior officer, irrespective of rank, was the 'Captain in Command' with all the powers, duties and responsibilities that position was accorded by King's Regulations and Admiralty Instructions.

Put succinctly, the Captain's prime duty was to ensure that what was being done at Fairlie was what the Royal Navy wanted done. But as will be seen, that duty was not always easy to fulfil.

The experimental work of the Establishment was carried out by what the Navy List referred to as 'civilian staff'. This group undertook the research and was the overall responsibility of the Chief Scientist, a post always filled at Fairlie by a civil servant in Admiralty employment. His role was to manage the often-competing interests of the Royal Navy, which wanted quick workable solutions to the U-boat problem, and those of his fellow scientists who often wanted to do more research to ensure new developments did really work – again not always an easy task. To add further difficulty, the Chief Scientist was directed in his duties by no less than three different Admiralty departments – Scientific Research, Anti-Submarine Warfare and Anti-Submarine Material.

The Establishment's operation was organised by the Chief Scientist into five main divisions – Research, Experiment & Development, Design, Electronics, and Laboratory. Each of these was in turn subdivided into specific project tasks. In usual civil servant form there was a hierarchy of up to eleven staff grades with positions ranging from Principal Scientific Officer through Senior Scientific Officer, Scientific Officer – and more – to the lowest grade at the bottom of the pecking order, Temporary Experimental Officer.

The senior positions were initially filled by prewar career scientists with long experience of working at *Osprey* and other Admiralty research establishments such as those at Shandon and Harwich, but the Temporary Experimental Officer grade mainly comprised very bright young science graduates taken on for the duration of the war. Some of these had volunteered in the normal way for military service while others were 'recommended' to the Admiralty through academics familiar with *Osprey*'s work. Twenty-three scientific staff moved from Portland to Fairlie in 1940. By the end of March 1945 the number of scientists working at the Establishment had soared to eighty-three, including four women.

The third group of employees comprised technicians and craftsmen of many different trades. Led by a Chief Technical Officer, it was their job to construct the prototypes of the scientists' ideas – 'turning their lash-ups into something that could work', as one man put it. Wood and metal workers, model makers, draftsmen, electricians, mechanics, and more. A particularly skilled and technical activity undertaken at Fairlie was the assembly of the asdic oscillators. Cementing the quartz and steel discs together required great precision and at one point six young women were engaged on this critical work under the watchful eye of one of the scientists responsible. Unfortunately, unlike the naval and scientific staff, no name list of this group of employees has been found and it can only be surmised that it included men transferred from Portland, local craftsmen such as those who had been employed in the Bay Street boatyard by William Fife, and other skilled men and women from elsewhere in Scotland.

'Miscellaneous' might be the best term for the fourth group. Again, no record appears to exist providing names or duties of this group. It is likely that some would be Royal Navy ratings and include men and women assisting the Captain and his officers with secretarial, transport and messing functions. Others, such as the Establishment policemen and payroll staff, would be Admiralty employees, while the majority are likely to have been recruited locally from Fairlie and nearby towns. They would include seamen and other boat handlers, general handy-men, cooks, cleaners and drivers, as well as telephonists, secretarial and postal staff. In 1944 an average of 500 letters and documents were being sent out each month from Fairlie to other Admiralty and Royal Navy shore establishments – every one having to be typed and cop-ied many times. The Establishment also received a large number of military and civilian visitors. During 1944 these visitors averaged an astonishing eighty a month. Each of them had to be met, transported, accommodated and generally looked after during their time in Fairlie.

As the war progressed, the number of people working at the Establishment in all four categories continued to increase. By the time of Germany's defeat the total number of men and women employed had risen to 285 – equivalent to about 30 per cent of Fairlie's prewar adult population.

The first two of the four groups – the Royal Navy officers and the civilian scientists – are now looked at further, for no other reason than they are the only two of the four about which any great detail can currently be found. Starting with the Senior Service, four Royal Navy officers occupied the post of Captain in Command of the Establishment, with each passing over the 'ship' to his successor as they took up their next appointment. Perhaps a surprising number for a five-year period, but it must be appreciated that, as Admiralty policy was that Royal Navy officer appointments should not last for more than two years, four captains in post between January 1941 and February 1946 was not unusual for both ships and shore bases.

All four of the Fairlie captains were career officers who had entered the Royal Navy as young boys from school and were aged in their mid-forties when taking command of the Establishment. As very junior officers in their mid-teens, two had been on warships which had taken part in the 1916 Battle of Jutland – the last major surface ship battle of the First World War. As their careers progressed, they had served in various sea-going and shore positions, but, most significantly, they had also undergone one or more periods of anti-submarine training and teaching at HMS *Osprey* in Portland. Thus all four were quite familiar with underwater acoustics and the challenges of detecting and sinking submarines. They would also have been well known to each other. Before the Second World War, anti-submarine specialism was not the most popular of the Navy's career branches and those who did choose it formed a relatively small group of officers.

Lieutenant-Commander William Francis Hollins was the first Royal Navy officer to serve as Captain of HM Anti-Submarine Experimental Establishment Fairlie. Hollins had joined the Navy in 1915 at the age of fourteen and saw sea-going service in various warships before becoming one of the early group of young officers to attend the anti-submarine course at Portland. In 1938 he obtained his first command as Captain of the Clyde-built sloop HMS *Puffin* (a sister ship of HMS *Kingfisher*, of which more later), which was then engaged on anti-submarine training exercises at HMS *Osprey*. With *Osprey*'s sudden move to the Clyde at the end of 1940, he took up the appointment at Fairlie in January 1941. He served there as Captain until May of that year. After his relatively short time at Fairlie, Hollins commanded the anti-submarine frigate HMS *Bideford* on anti-submarine training and convoy escort duties, and in April 1945 he was appointed the first Captain of the new Dumbarton-built sloop HMS *Opossum*. He retired from the Navy in 1946.

Experimental Department.

(*Postal Address*:—*The Commanding Officer, H.M. A/S Experimental Establishment, Fairlie, Ayrshire.*)

Lieut.-Com. ....W. F. Hollins .... 11 Mar 40
(A/S) H. C. K. Melville
RAN (*act*) .... 1 May 39
Tempy.
Lieut. Com., }H. E. Shaxted (*act*)......... 2 Aug 40
R.N.V.R.
Lieutenant ....A. W. Goldsmith........... 28 Nov 40
Paym.
Sub-Lieut., }J. P. C. King................. 7 Feb 40
R.N.V.R.

The Navy List dates back to the eighteenth century and provides information about all serving Royal Navy officers. Normally an annual publication, during the Second World War it was updated more frequently. This extract shows those attached to the Fairlie part of HMS *Osprey* in early 1941.

Hollins' successor at Fairlie was Captain Newton James Wallop William-Powlett. As his name suggests, he was a member of a Hampshire aristocratic family listed in Debrett's Peerage with a long military history. Born in 1896, he joined the Royal Navy as a boy entrant in 1909. In May 1916 William-Powlett was serving as a sub-lieutenant on the destroyer HMS *Tipperary* when as part of the 4th Destroyer Flotilla she was searching for the German High Seas Fleet in the North Sea. During the engagement that followed, *Tipperary* was repeatedly hit by shells from the enemy battleships and quickly turned into a blazing wreck with the loss of 185 of her 197 crew. William-Powlett

HMS *Tipperary* was only a year old when she was sunk early on the morning of 1 June 1916, one of fourteen Royal Navy warships lost during the Battle of Jutland. The inconclusive outcome of this last great surface fleet battle of the First World War resulted in Germany concentrating on the deployment of the U-boat. This photo is of one of HMS *Tipperary*'s identical sister destroyers, HMS *Botha*.

was one of the few survivors and for his efforts to save the lives of other crew members was awarded a Distinguished Service Cross. He was also recommended for early promotion, the Flotilla Captain writing: 'I cannot speak too highly of this young officer's conduct.'

After the war was over, William-Powlett specialised in anti-submarine warfare at Portland and had periods serving on the battleship HMS *Nelson* and the aircraft carrier HMS *Courageous*. In 1939 he was Commanding Officer of the cruiser HMS *Calypso* before returning to Portland in 1940 as Captain of HMS *Osprey*. He was thus the natural choice to take charge at Fairlie after Hollins and served as the Establishment's Captain from

June 1941 to July 1942. Following that appointment he commanded the training cruiser HMS *Dauntless* and then in September 1943 the New Zealand Navy's 1942-built cruiser HMS *Gambia*. Newton William-Powlett retired from the Royal Navy in 1948 after a year serving as a Naval Aide-de-Camp to King George VI, and died in 1963. His younger brother Peveril also served with distinction in the Navy and became a Vice-Admiral and another Naval Aide-de-Camp to the King.

From August 1942 to January 1944 the Establishment was the responsibility of Captain Peter Grenville Lyon Cazalet. Born in 1899 and, like his predecessor, coming from a long line of military officers, Cazalet served as a midshipman during the First World War on the battleship HMS *Princess Royal*, also involved at Jutland, and again later specialised in anti-submarine tactics. As well as periods instructing at *Osprey*, in the 1930s he commanded the destroyers HMS *Viscount* and HMS *Hero*. In June 1940 he was awarded the Distinguished Service Cross for his action during an attempt to destroy key port installations in Holland and Belgium before the Germans could seize them. Prior to taking command at Fairlie, Cazalet was in charge of the asdic training base HMS *Nimrod* at Campbeltown.

After his service at the Establishment, Cazalet held appointments as commanding officer of various destroyers engaged in escorting the convoys round the North Cape to Russia, for which he was awarded the Distinguished Service Order. When the war was over, he later took command of the twenty-year-old County-class cruiser HMS *London*. This ship became well known to the British public when she attempted to assist the frigate HMS *Amethyst* escape down the Yangtse River after being attacked by the Communist Chinese in 1949. During the action, HMS *London* was heavily shelled

Captain Peter Cazalet, the Establishment's third commanding officer.

HMS London after her return down the Yangtse River to Shanghai. The twelve
crew members who died were interred at the International Cemetery.

by the Chinese shore batteries. Twelve of her crew were killed and
many wounded, among the latter being Captain Cazalet. The story
of the rescue of HMS *Amethyst* was later dramatised in the film *Yangtse
Incident*. In 1950 Cazalet was appointed Rear Admiral and yet another
Naval Aide-de-Camp to the King. In 1953 he was promoted Vice
Admiral and in 1955, two years before retirement from the Navy, he
became Sir Peter. All of which shows what twenty months' service at
Fairlie can do for a sailor's career!

Ronald John Robert Dendy took over command of the Establishment
after Peter Cazalet at the end of February 1944 and remained as Captain
until its closure in February 1946. Born in 1900, Dendy's early naval
career was similar to that of his predecessors, with First World War

service being followed by specialism in anti-submarine warfare, and training appointments at *Osprey*. In December 1941, however, he was the Second in Command of the battlecruiser HMS *Repulse* when, along with Britain's newest battleship HMS *Prince of Wales*, his ship was sunk by Japanese aircraft off the east coast of Malaya (Malaysia). After being rescued and returned to Britain, Dendy was given command of the cruiser HMS *Coventry*, only to have that ship also sink from under him following attack by German planes in the southern Mediterranean in September 1942. Following such traumatic events, his appointment to the dry and relatively peaceful command of HM A/S Experimental Establishment Fairlie was one he would perhaps have appreciated. After his two years as Captain at Fairlie, Dendy held an appointment as senior British naval officer in the Persian Gulf before retiring from the service in 1951.

Other Royal Navy officers were posted to the Establishment to assist the Captain. These varied in number over the years between three and nine. Some were Royal Navy or Royal Naval Reserve but others served with the Royal Naval Volunteer Reserve and had joined or been called up for the duration of hostilities. The duties of these officers included arranging the use of Royal Navy vessels to assist with asdic and weapon trials, and supervising the fitting of asdic equipment to new warships. This latter work involved extensive travelling throughout Britain. Mostly this was by train, but the family of one former Establishment employee recall their father tell of driving officers to faraway naval bases and shipyards at all hours of the day and night. Further naval support is believed to have been

Anti-Submarine Experimental Establishment.

(Postal address—*The Captain,*
H.M. A/SE Establishment, Fairlie, Ayrshire.)

Captain..............R. J. R. Dendy.............. 21 Feb 44
(*In Command.*)

Tempy.
Lieut.-Com., }S. Houghton, OBE, FRSA... 30 Oct 39
R.N.V.R.

Lieutenant.........(A/S) L. A. Rogers........... — July 43
(A/S) D. E. Payne........... 4 Sept 44

Tempy. Elect.
Lieut.-Com., }W. G. Huggett (act)......... 24 Nov 43
R.N.V.R.

Tempy.   } J. G. Horn.................... 16 Feb 42
Elect. Lieut., } H. C. Pollard................. 24 Sept 43
R.N.V.R.   } G. M. S. Nayler............. 17 Apr 44
(*For Application duties.*)
F. W. Ralph.................. 24 Jan 44
R. W. Clegg.................. 6 Mar 44
(*For Application duties as A/S EE.*)
(*For Civilian Staff see page 2225.*)

Royal Navy officers of the Establishment as in the Navy List autumn 1944.

provided by five Norwegian Navy officers who had crossed the North Sea in a small boat after the Germans had invaded their country.

Two of the retired Royal Navy officers who served at the Establishment were particularly well known in Fairlie. Commander John ('Jack') Alexander Binnie was born in 1898 and, after active service during the First World War, specialised in anti-submarine warfare and asdic training at Portland. Binnie retired from the Navy in 1931 but seven years later was asked by William-Powlett to return to *Osprey* to make use of his asdic expertise. After moving to Fairlie, Binnie resumed his studies into the practical application of asdic and the challenges faced by the asdic operators at sea. He made a number of Arctic voyages aboard a Royal Navy warship to study the thermocline effect. On 11 March 1945 along with other specialist anti-submarine officers he boarded the frigate HMS *Lapwing* which then sailed as part of the escort of one of the last Russian convoys of the war. Nine days later *Lapwing* was torpedoed by *U-968* just five miles away from the destination port of Murmansk. Very sadly, Binnie died together with many members of the frigate's crew – just fifty days before VE Day. One of the other warships escorting that convoy to Russia was the new destroyer HMS *Myngs*, commanded by Binnie's fellow Fairlie officer Peter Cazalet.

During his time serving at Fairlie, Jack Binnie lived locally with his wife and two daughters and was a member of St Columba's Scottish Episcopal Church in Largs. After his death a memorial service was held in the church, which was attended by almost all of the Establishment staff and many local people. One of those at the service described it as 'beautifully done' with singing of the old seafaring hymns – 'a most heart rending service'. Binnie's name is at the top of the memorial within the Largs church to congregational members who died in the Second World War.

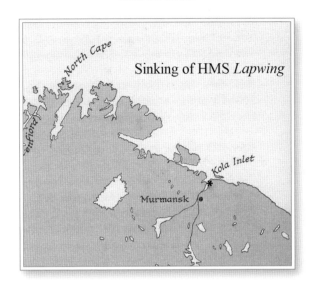

HMS *Lapwing* was a product of Scotts Shipbuilding & Engineering yard at Greenock and was only a year old when she was sunk in the Kola Inlet. She is shown here anchored at Loch Ewe after returning from an earlier Arctic convoy. Between December 1942 and May 1945 eighteen Royal Navy warships were sunk while escorting convoys to Russia.

IN GRATEFUL REMEMBRANCE
OF THE MEMBERS OF THIS
CONGREGATION WHO LAID
DOWN THEIR LIVES IN THE
WORLD WAR   1939–1945

BINNIE, J. A.   COMMANDER, R. N.

(*Left*) Commander John Binnie during his time of service at Fairlie. (*Right*) The memorial plaque in Largs St Columba's Episcopal Church.

Lieutenant-Commander Sydney Charles Houghton was another Royal Navy officer brought back from retirement to assist with the wartime asdic research. Houghton was a college graduate in his early twenties when in 1914 he enlisted as a member of the Royal Naval Volunteer Reserve. At college he appears to have taken some interest in the developing science of acoustics and it was in this specialist area that his volunteered expertise was used by the Navy. In 1916 his then superior officer – Newton William-Powlett – recommended him for a command 'for good service' and in July 1917 the Admiralty sent him to the United States to learn what the Americans were doing on the acoustic detection of submarines. After his return to Britain, Houghton was promoted to Lieutenant-Commander and on retiring from the Navy in 1919 was appointed OBE 'for valuable service in connection with a method of detection of submarines'.

No further information about Houghton's life could be found until he joined the staff of HMS *Osprey* in 1939 with the rank of Temporary Lieutenant-Commander (retired) RNVR, again probably at the request of William-Powlett. In December 1940 he moved from Portland to Fairlie and continued as one of the Establishment's naval staff right through until almost the end of the war. By all accounts he was very popular, both with those who worked there and with the Fairlie residents, and appears to have taken on the role of what might be termed today 'the community liaison officer' for the Establishment. Said to be known to the locals as 'Uncle Sid', he lived for most of his time in Fairlie in a small seafront cottage in Ferry Row. Houghton was much involved with war effort fund-raising and local community events. He was also described in the local newspaper as 'a not unknown artist who attracts considerable attention' (the initials FRSA followed OBE in his Navy List name) and is said to have produced many watercolour paintings of Fairlie scenes. These were sold in the village post office for five shillings – about twenty pounds in today's value – in aid of wartime charities. Who in Fairlie might still have one of Houghton's paintings on their wall?

Unlike the civilian staff of the Establishment, the Royal Navy officers were provided with official accommodation. Two of Fairlie's oldest and largest houses were taken over for this purpose. Both were located at the south end of the village and conveniently close to one of Fairlie's railway stations. The property of Brookside was used as the Captain's house, while the nearby and more extensive property of Fairlieburne was where the single officers slept, ate and relaxed – being in effect the officers' mess. After moving into Fairlieburne the Navy erected various Nissen huts – semi-circular corrugated iron structures – in the extensive grounds, which were used by the Royal Navy technical officers for storing and adjusting asdic equipment.

In Fairlieburne, naval ratings looked after the officers with a Wren Chief Petty Officer in charge. When formal dinners were held, for example on Trafalgar Night, all present were required to wear mess dress or dinner jackets, as they would if aboard any Royal Navy ship on that night. During the course of the war many naval officers from Canada, Australia, the United States and elsewhere made visits to the Establishment and where possible they were accommodated in Fairlieburne. One frigate captain who stayed at the house on several occasions described it as 'a fine old country home, magnificent

Fairlieburne, one of the large seafront houses built in Fairlie in Victorian times, was used to house officers during the Second World War. After the war, it became a popular local hotel and restaurant but was later demolished and the site redeveloped for housing.

gardens, panelled rooms – the most genteel of living during meals and in the evening'. Another reported that he and his fellow officers were 'waited on hand and foot by amiable Wrens' and enjoyed 'good drinks and warm and comfortable quarters'. All a far cry from the conditions which some of the officers faced when hunting U-boats in the North Atlantic or escorting the Arctic convoys in winter.

Brookside, the adjoining older house, was the home of the Establishment's Captain in Command. Three of the Captains had their families staying with them during their time in Fairlie. As with any Royal Navy command, the Captain had naval ratings, including Wrens, to look after the house. He also had a junior officer as his secretary or personal assistant. A Fairlie lady now in her eighties remembers as a young girl playing in Brookside with Captain Dendy's daughter, while Newton William-Powlett's wife and children are said to have much enjoyed their months in the village. Peter Cazalet's grandson recalls his father telling of his time as a thirteen-year-old staying in Brookside with his naval father, particularly being taken sailing in a small dinghy

The Establishment's Royal Navy Captains in Command
stayed in Brookside. It is still a family home.

Royal Navy officers of the Establishment in July 1945. Captain Dendy is on
the far right. Lieutenant-Commander Houghton is sixth from left. The Wren is
believed to be Anne Hampton, Captain Dendy's personal assistant.

in Fairlie Bay by his father's coxswain – an activity forbidden to every
other Fairlie resident during the war.

Turning to the scientists, those in charge of the Establishment's
research and experimental work over the five years were Benjamin
Smith, John ('Jock') Roberts and Jack Anderson. All of these men had
long experience of government research work. Benjamin Spalding
Smith was born in South Australia in 1887 and, after moving to
London, studied for a degree in electrical engineering. He is first noted

as working on acoustics when employed as a technical assistant at Shandon on the Gare Loch at the end of the First World War, and thereafter joined the Admiralty on a permanent basis. In 1927 he was appointed the Chief Scientist at HMS *Osprey* and retained that post until, along with many of his Portland colleagues, he made the move to Fairlie in November 1940. At Fairlie he occupied the new position of Superintending Scientist. By then Smith was generally regarded as being the foremost authority on submarine detection by asdic in Britain, if not the world, and had been recognised as such by being appointed OBE in 1938. Among his many achievements was the development of the retractable dome for the asdic transducers.

By all accounts Smith was a very thorough and determined researcher and he expected similar dedication from those under him – at *Osprey*, for example, he insisted that every one of the scientists in his charge keep a detailed diary of each week's activities, which he regularly reviewed. This very rigorous approach to research was accepted by his career civil servant colleagues but started to cause some difficulty when the Establishment took on the younger scientists who had come fresh from university. They had no civil service experience and were accustomed by their academic training to question and challenge. This they frequently did while at Fairlie and found it very frustrating when Smith regularly rejected their suggestions, usually without explanation. One of the young men later described him as 'a first-class obstructionist who would not allow any ideas but his own to be heard', while another complained to a friend 'my encounters with the Chief Scientist on technical matters have been rich in criticism but lacking in help and encouragement'.

Smith also had difficulties with the Admiralty and the Royal Navy. Faced with mounting losses of the merchant ships bringing vital supplies and equipment across the Atlantic, not unreasonably the Navy wanted the most effective asdic to help its escort vessels hunt and kill the U-boats. Thus Smith was under intense pressure to improve the various types as quickly as possible and for these to be made available as soon as a viable prototype had been developed. But scientists do not work like that. A scientist needs to understand why a new device does what it does based on extensive research into the theory as well as the practice. Smith frequently upset his Royal Navy colleagues by complaining that they gave the scientists 'little opportunity for systematic research on the fundamental conditions that control the asdic method of detection'. It was the difficulty of maintaining the balance between research and application which had resulted some years before in the formation of the Admiralty Research Laboratory at Teddington with a scientist in charge, and the Experimental Establishment at Portland, and later Fairlie, where a Royal Navy captain was in command.

The growing friction between Smith and the younger members of the Establishment staff came to a head in the summer of 1942 with pressure from some of them for Smith to be replaced. Two wrote a long letter to the Admiralty listing their complaints about Smith's leadership and asserting that 'the majority of the Establishment's staff lack confidence in the administration', adding that 'over one third of the temporary [experimental] officers have requested a transfer elsewhere'. However, Smith had strong support from the Establishment's then Captain, William-Powlett, who having worked with him at Portland considered him to be a scientist 'who understood the Navy'.

But the number of complaints could not be ignored and Smith did depart from his position at Fairlie in August 1942. While it has been stated in some contemporary accounts that his going was much against his will, National Archive records show that prior to his alleged 'removal' he had been selected by the Admiralty to be Britain's acoustic warfare special representative in the United States. So might it be that the complaints were part of an Admiralty deception to avoid revealing the collaboration? It will never now be known. In his new role Smith made a number of Atlantic crossings without any of his ships being torpedoed, which must have been a cause of some satisfaction. After the war was over, Benjamin Smith continued his distinguished scientific career both as a civil servant and in retirement. He died in 1984 at the age of ninety-seven – not a bad age for a 'first-class obstructionist'.

Smith was succeeded as Superintending Scientist by forty-five-year-old John Keith Roberts. Also born in Australia, Roberts was a chemist by training whose early career included research at Cambridge University and the Cavendish Laboratory where he became a leading expert on the absorption of gases by metal surfaces. In 1939 he volunteered for naval service as a scientific officer and was first employed on research into acoustic mines – those which exploded not from contact with a ship but from the noise made as it passed by. In August 1942 he was asked to take over from Smith and assume charge of the increasing complexity and range of the research being carried out at Fairlie at this very critical stage of the U-boat war. This he did with great effect, completely reorganising the Establishment's methods of working. He achieved an excellent working relationship with Captain Cazalet, although less so with some of the older scientists still loyal to Smith. But his workload – including a visit to New York in the late summer of 1943 to give a further update to the United States Navy on Britain's asdic developments – was extremely arduous and his health soon suffered. In March 1944 John Roberts developed pneumonia and died in a London hospital a month later.

Roberts' untimely death was a major blow to the Establishment, with its ever-increasing workload, so it was imperative that he was replaced quickly. This was achieved by promoting Jack ('Jock') Anderson from his existing position of Chief Technical Officer at Fairlie. Like Smith, Anderson had worked at Shandon and Harwich as a young assistant to the Canadian physicist Robert Boyle, generally credited with developing the first oscillator to both transmit and receive sound waves – in effect the 'asdic'. After moving to Portland, Anderson continued with asdic research and in 1932 took charge of the asdic section at HMS *Osprey*. He had particular responsibility for the sea trials of the different types then being developed and for the design of the underwater domes housing the asdic transducers, their shape having a very critical effect on the sound transmission. On one occasion Anderson positioned himself in an observation chamber fitted below the hull of the cruiser HMS *Devonshire* from where he could view the flow path and turbulence created by the asdic dome positioned ahead. As *Devonshire* could sail at 30 knots this was a somewhat dangerous experiment, but it did produce very valuable information.

After his promotion at Fairlie in 1944, Anderson retained the post of Superintending Scientist until the Navy's acoustic research returned to Portland. Unlike his colleague Smith, Anderson was a born people organiser. He was also much trusted and liked by the Navy for his down-to-earth approach to the Establishment's work, effectively maintaining a fair balance between the scientists' fundamental research on underwater acoustics and the asdic's practical development as a vital Royal Navy anti-submarine tool. After the war, Anderson continued in Admiralty employment and in 1959 became head of the newly formed Admiralty Surface Weapons Establishment at Portsdown Hill in Hampshire.

As the U-boat offensives intensified and presented new challenges to Fairlie it became necessary to greatly expand the scientific and experimental staff far beyond those who had moved north from HMS *Osprey*. Very much in demand were young men and women with a university degree in some aspect of science or mathematics. As mentioned earlier, these were recruited as Temporary Experimental Officers by a process then common to almost all wartime government research establishments – including the code-breaking Bletchley Park – and was very much based on some personal recommendation from an academic privy to who was wanted where and for what. This process has been described by one young man as 'first being invited to an interview by prominent people' and, if acceptable, some days later receiving a buff envelope containing a letter of appointment and a travel warrant with the instruction 'to take a certain train on a certain day to a certain place'. It was only on being met on his arrival at the specified place that he was told what he was going to be doing there. Thus one can

Two of the Establishment's
Temporary Experimental Officers –
how young they look!

imagine a steady stream of young men from 1941 onwards and a few women – being met off the train at Fairlie Station and taken to Fairlieburne or the Establishment's offices in Bay Street.

Their early time at the Establishment could be confusing for some of the young men. After a couple of weeks at Fairlie one of the new boys expressed the opinion that he thought that one of his colleagues 'was not exactly fitted for anti-submarine work', and quickly added 'but then neither are any of us – Fairlie seems to be the sort of place they shipped scientists they didn't know what to do with'. While the rapid introduction of youngsters fresh from university to a very hierarchal civil servant system might well have been better managed, there can be no doubt that overall the new blood provided both stimulus and expertise.

Recruitment was not restricted to young graduates or, surprisingly, to British citizens. Older scientists also joined the Establishment's staff. Paul Vigoureux was born of French parents in Mauritius and, after coming to Britain, studied metrology – the science of precise measurement. He joined HMS *Osprey* in 1938 and worked at Fairlie as a Principal Scientific Officer throughout the war. He was described by colleagues as 'a perfectionist, but kindly, austere, well liked and courteous'. Outwith work he was much involved in a drama club formed by the Establishment staff. After Fairlie, Vigoureux continued his research at other Admiralty and government research laboratories. Best known for his contribution to the introduction of the SI units of measurement, he died in 1999 at the age of ninety-six.

After graduating from King's College, London, with a degree in chemistry in 1926, George Deacon worked for a government organisation called the Discovery Committee whose principal aim was to study the scientific properties of the seas of the Southern Ocean. Deacon participated in four expeditions to this inhospitable part of the world before being recruited to Portland in 1939, and then coming north to Fairlie. His expertise was in the physical properties of the sea and his many measurements of salinity and temperature helped explain the existence of the thermoclines which had been found to distort asdic beams. At Fairlie he helped develop an improved type of bathythermograph, an instrument which could measure and record sea temperature variations over considerable depths, and in October 1943 he undertook studies using one of these instruments from a warship escorting a convoy to Russia. In 1944 Deacon transferred to another Admiralty establishment specialising in the new science of oceanography and five years later became the first Director of the UK's National Institute of Oceanography, later rebranded as the Institute of Oceanographic Science. He was knighted in 1971.

Another distinguished member of the Establishment's 'alumni' was Francis Thomas Bacon. Born in 1904, Bacon attended Eton College and graduated from Cambridge University with an engineering degree. His lifetime interest was in the development of the alkali fuel cell – a compact device able to create electricity from mixing hydrogen and oxygen. The crowning success of Bacon's expertise in fuel cells was the installation of such cells on the Apollo 11 spacecraft, which enabled the first human landing on the moon in 1969. He received personal congratulations for his work on the project from both the astronauts and US President Nixon.

Tom Bacon found himself working at the Establishment throughout its five years at Fairlie. But working on what? The many obituaries and other stories of his life describe his activity between 1941 and

Three of the scientists who worked at the Establishment during the Second World War.
(*Above left*) George Deacon on a research vessel returning from one of the discovery voyages to the Southern Ocean.
(*Above right*) Tom Bacon, who during his years at Fairlie may have undertaken research on submarine fuel cells.
(*Left*) Paul Vigoureux, 'a perfectionist'.

1946 as no more than 'working for the Admiralty on asdic'. Unlike the other scientists who came to Fairlie, however, Bacon knew nothing about acoustics. But he did know a great deal about batteries and fuel cells, and in 1940 had suggested the possibility of using the latter as a means of propelling a submarine. There is no mention anywhere of Fairlie undertaking research into this possibility – indeed Hackman's book *Seek & Strike* does not even mention the subject or Bacon's name – but given its potential and his expertise it would not be surprising if Bacon worked on such a project during his years at Fairlie. If so, it would have been regarded as being of the greatest secrecy both during the Second World War and in the Cold War years which followed, and thus kept well away from any public record. Is this another secret of wartime Fairlie still to be uncovered? In the 1990s the first fuel-cell-powered submarines did come into service – as new U-boats with the German Navy.

While Deacon, Vigoureux and Bacon could be regarded as having followed the more common wartime route to joining the Establishment, their colleague Moshé Feldenkrais certainly did not. He was a Jew born in Ukraine in 1904, who to avoid persecution moved first to British-occupied Palestine and then to France. From 1928 he worked in what became the Curie Research Institute in Paris. When the German army invaded France it was decided to evacuate to Britain as many of the Institute's staff as wished to leave. Given his religion, Feldenkrais certainly wanted to leave and in June 1940 he was instructed to go quickly to Bordeaux carrying two large suitcases. With other refugees he boarded a British ship just hours before the Germans attacked, and after a hazardous voyage eventually reached London. On arrival, Feldenkrais found that one of his suitcases contained all of the Curie research notes on atomic fission, and the other a container of heavy water – a necessary ingredient of atomic bomb development as highlighted in the 1965 film *The Heroes of Telemark*. Sent to join the Establishment, he worked at Fairlie on the science of acoustics until the end of the war. In 1951 Feldenkrais emigrated to the new State of Israel. He became a senior officer in the Scientific Research Centre of the Israeli Defence Forces, but is perhaps better remembered today for his development of the Feldenkrais technique of fitness and relaxation.

The foregoing are only a few examples of the many civilian scientists who worked at Fairlie during the war. All were very clever – many quite brilliant – and some were very difficult for their colleagues to work with. After their time in the village, most went on to have eminent research careers in business, government and academia. Several were elected to the prestigious Fellowship of the Royal Society and others received knighthoods and similar distinction. Looking at accounts of their post-Fairlie careers, however, it is interesting that even after many years, few made more than a passing reference to their wartime work, or to their time in the village. As noted earlier in regard to Bacon, that interlude in their careers is described in most biographies and

H.M.S. 'OSPREY.'

Serving in H.M.A/S.E. Establishments, Fairlie, Ayrshire. Telephone, Fairlie 317 (three lines) and 208.

Civilian Staff.

Superintending Scientist—
J. Anderson, OBE, AMIEE ... ... —

Principal Scientific Officers—
N. D. Astbury, MA, FInstP, AMIEE (act) —
J. Colquhoun, MSC, BEng, AMIEE (act) ... 5 Apr 27
A. C. Law, MA (act) ... ... —
P. Vigoureux, BSC, DIC, PhD (act) ... 8 Aug 38
H. F. Willis, MSC, PhD (act), Esqrs. ... —

†Senior Scientific Officers—
W. E. Dawson, MSC (act) ... ... 1 Sept 38
T. Emmerson, BSC, PhD (act) ... ... —
J. H. Hakes, BSC (act) ... ... —
D. A. Hanley, BA (act) ... ... —
W. W. Jackson, MSC, PhD (act) ... 3 May 36
L. R. G. Samphier, AMIEE, ACGI, DIC (act) 7 June 27

Senior Technical Officer—
E. B. D. Mackenzie, Esq., BSc ... ... 25 May 27

†Scientific Officers—
F. G. Apthorpe (act) ... ... —
K. F. Bowden, MSC (act) ... ... —
S. A. Byard (act) ... ... —
A. Freedman, BSC (act) ... ... —
R. R. Wilson (act), Esqrs. ... ... —

Senior Naturalist—
H. Wood, Esq., MA, PhD ... ... —

Chief Technical Officer—
A. E. H. Pew, OBE ... ... —

Principal Technical Officer—
J. O. Davis, Esq. (act) ... ... —

Senior Technical Officer—
H. E. Stoakes, Esq. (act) ... ... —

†Technical Officers—
J. W. G. Clarke, BSC(Eng) ... ... —
B. O. B. Gamble, BSC ... ... —
S. A. McKay ... ... —
W. J. McCarthy, (act) ... ... —
J. G. Rees (act), Esqrs. ... ... —

Temporary Senior Experimental Officers—
E. A. Alexander, PhD ... ... —
W. E. Benton, MSC ... ... —
B. C. Browne, MA ... ... —
J. W. Fisher, BSC, PhD, MRCS, LRCP ... —
J. G. Horn, BSC (Eng), AMIEE, ASSOC.AIEE —
J. H. Lansdell, Esqrs.

Temporary Experimental Officers—
R. T. Ackroyd, BEng ... ...
J. W. Almond ... ...
F. T. Bacon, BA ... ...
D. W. Boston, BSC ... ...
W. Brass, MA ... ...
W. M. Colles, MA ... ...
D. H. Crawford, BSC ... ...
G. C. Curtis, IA ... ...
M. Feldenkrais ... ...
H. J. Fountain ... ...
F. Foxcroft, BSC ... ...
T. M. Fry ... ...
J. R. B. Greer ... ...
E. Gresty, BSC, AMIEE ... ...
F. T. Gubbens ... ...
R. Hall, BA ... ...
W. Halliday, BEng ... ...
M. H. J. Hawkins, BSC ... ...
G. F. Hodsman, BSC ... ...
A. J. Howie, MA, Esqrs. ... ...
Miss G. M. Johnson, MA ... ...
R. L. Kay, AHWC ... ...
J. McFarlane, BSC ... ...
J. McD. McGlashan, MA ... ...
J. W. Menter, BA ... ...
H. K. Moneypenny, ASC, ARCS ...
G. W. A. Morris, BSC ... ...
E. J. W. Morrison, BSC ... ...
P. C. Newman ... ...
A. Nightingale, BA ... ...
R. Q. A. Packard, BSC ... ...
T. M. Palmer, FHDipHons ...
J. G. T. Paterson, BSC ... ...
H. J. Phear... ... ...
L. Rhoden, BSC ... ...
E. L. Robinson ... ...
F. A. Rushworth, BSC, ARCS ...
A. B. Scott-Wilson, FIA ... ...
R. B. Serle ... ...
G. A. Smith, BSC ... ...
A. Stewart, MA ... ...
B. T. Taylor, BSC ... ...
C. A. Teer, BSC ... ...
G. H. Townend, BEng ... ...
D. Walker, Esqrs. ... ...
Miss E. L. Walker, MA, BSC ... ...
A. Watson, Esq., BSC ... ...
Mrs. M. I. Willis, BSC ... ...
Mrs. M. Wilson, BSC ... ...
P. B. Wilson, MA, AInstP, ...
P. Wootton, BSC, Esqrs. ... ...

The scientific staff of the Establishment as in the April 1945 Navy List. Four of the fifty-one Temporary Experimental Officers are women.

obituaries only as 'on Admiralty service at Fairlie' or in similar vague terms. That signing of the Official Secrets Act was never forgotten.

While some information about the Royal Navy officers and the scientific staff of the Establishment has been found, little has been discovered about those who in so many ways supported the research and experimental work. No list of names, occupations or addresses has come to light and it is now only through a few remembrances given to family or friends that experiences can be related. The secret nature of the work and the passage of the years has meant that memories have faded, people have passed away, and letters and diaries, if kept, have got lost. While many of the technical staff were highly skilled tradesmen, and some were Royal Navy career artificers, for others much of the work they did in and around the Bay Street yard was quite mundane. Answering telephones, driving, typing, filing, moving equipment whose purpose could not be revealed even if it was known, ferrying men to and from the Establishment's research vessels, were not activities conducive to inclusion in published wartime recollections from those who saw active service in the armed forces.

Researching the lives and careers of the naval officers and the scientists who worked at the Establishment during the war has been both time consuming and very interesting. Interesting – indeed fascinating – because of the social differences which became apparent between these incomers to Fairlie and those from the old families who had been born and raised in the village. Before 1939 Fairlie was a quite small community with a population of around 1,000. Other than shopkeepers and tradespeople, local employment in the main came from William Fife & Son's boatyard, the railway, the railway pier and the two stations, and looking after the big houses along the shore front. A small number of the newer residents travelled each day to Nobel's Explosive Works down the coast at Ardeer, or by train to work in Glasgow. That population mix changed dramatically with the arrival of the Royal Navy and its many scientific advisers. How did the locals interact with those who were always described as 'our friends from the south' – if indeed they did? We look at this in Chapter 7, but first let us look at the ships that supported the Establishment's work.

Chapter 6

THE SHIPS

'Ospreys and a Kingfisher'

All of the anti-submarine research and experimental studies undertaken at the Establishment during its five years in Fairlie related to activities below the surface of the sea. The proximity of the Bay Street site to the sheltered waters of Fairlie Bay and to the deeper areas of the Firth of Clyde and beyond was thus one of the main reasons for the selection of Fairlie as part of the wartime replacement for Portland's HMS *Osprey*. Testing the scientists' theories through full-scale experiments at sea was an essential part of the Establishment's work. To progress this testing, use had to be made of both surface ships and submarines. While some of the vessels were made available by the Royal Navy as and when required, for much of the war, five ships were permanently based at Fairlie and operated under the direct control of the Establishment's naval and civilian staff. These ships became familiar sights to local people when they were moored in Fairlie Bay or when seen sailing to and from operations further afield. But very few of those who watched would know what the role of these ships had been – even long after the war had ended and Fairlie Bay had returned to its traditional use as a safe anchorage for pleasure yachts.

Two of the five vessels most associated with the Establishment were Royal Navy warships and three were merchant ships requisitioned by the government for the duration of the war. The requisitioning, or taking over, of merchant ships either by the Admiralty or by the

Ministry of War Transport was very common as it provided quick access to a wide range of ships which could be used to assist the Royal Navy. Some, such as the Clyde paddle steamers which were used as minesweepers, were given the status of an HMS name, but most served as auxiliary support craft in a wide range of rolls, usually with no name change.

The first merchant ship to be requisitioned for use at Fairlie was a very elderly iron-built cargo steamer – iron being preferable to steel for acoustic studies. Launched from the Aberdeen shipyard of Hall, Russell & Company in 1872 with the name *Spray*, she was typical of the many hundreds of small ships that were engaged in carrying bulk cargoes like coal and grain around the British coast and across the Irish Sea. As such she passed through the hands of various owners until acquired in 1932 by a Liverpool company who renamed her *Dunvegan*. Under this name she continued in the coastal trade until taken under Admiralty control in January 1941 for service at Fairlie as a floating laboratory for hydrophone and asdic experiments.

The steam coaster *Dunvegan* seen departing from the Irish port of Waterford in the 1930s after delivering a cargo of coal.

A rare Second World War photo of *Dunvegan* moored in Fairlie Bay
after her conversion to a floating asdic laboratory.

The role of the 181-foot-long *Dunvegan* was to be a static one – in
effect a hulk. At a Liverpool shipyard her cargo holds were converted
for use as laboratories and then fitted out with specialist and valuable
equipment transferred from Portland. The work complete, *Dunvegan*
arrived in the Clyde in March 1941 where she was attached to permanent moorings laid in Fairlie Bay just off the Establishment. To
provide the high-voltage electricity needed to power the asdic types
being tested, undersea cables were laid between the ship and the shoreside generators as well as a telephone line. In addition to the daily
visits of the scientists and technicians who worked in her former holds,
Dunvegan was manned for much of her time at Fairlie by four Welsh
seamen – one of whom is believed to have married a local Fairlie girl.
Because of her valuable equipment, *Dunvegan* was purchased by the
Admiralty in January 1945 and when the war was over she was towed
south to Portland. Here she continued to support anti-submarine
acoustic research until broken up for scrap in 1958 at the venerable
age of eighty-six years.

To assist with the positioning of hydrophones, asdic targets and
other seabed apparatus in the waters off Fairlie and elsewhere in
the Clyde, a second cargo ship was requisitioned in February 1941
'for anti-submarine services'. With a length of 121 feet, the steamer
Pandora was somewhat smaller than *Dunvegan*, and more akin to a

Dunvegan's main cargo hold after conversion to a floating asdic laboratory.

Experiments being carried out from *Dunvegan* while moored in Fairlie Bay.

large Clyde puffer. *Pandora* had been built on the Tyne in 1893 and, like *Dunvegan*, was mainly employed carrying coal and other bulk cargoes around the coast of the British Isles. On her requisition, it was found that the name *Pandora* was already in use by the Royal Navy for one of its P-class submarines. To avoid any confusion, the requisitioned *Pandora* had to be renamed. The choice of name, *Icewhale*, was made with some sense of history. As described earlier, the small warship named HMS *Icewhale* was one of the first Royal Navy vessels to be fitted with asdic when she was part of the Portland-based 1st Anti-Submarine Flotilla, and in 1924 she was renamed HMS *Osprey*. Under both names she would have been very familiar to scientists like Smith and Anderson who came from Portland, which probably explains the choice of *Icewhale* as the new name for *Pandora*.

Icewhale, ex *Pandora*, undertook a wide range of work while based at Fairlie. Used for laying and lifting moorings and test equipment, recovering practice projectiles and positioning targets, she usually berthed at Fairlie Pier to load and discharge her cargo of strange objects. She also

The small coaster *Pandora* was given the name *Icewhale* for the duration of her Admiralty service at Fairlie.

Icewhale installing a seabed structure in the Firth of Clyde.
The very complicated arrangement of shapes was designed by the Fairlie
scientists to reproduce the acoustic signature of a U-boat.

acted at times as a more mobile asdic testing platform than *Dunvegan*. She could often be found in the deeper-water asdic test areas such as off the island of Inchmarnock and in the Kilbrannan Sound to the west of Arran. Her Admiralty work at Fairlie over, *Icewhale* was returned to her owners in 1946. She then resumed the name *Pandora* and went back to her interrupted coastal cargo carrying. Regrettably, she foundered in heavy weather north of Whitby in 1951 with the loss of six of her crew.

The third merchant vessel to support the research at Fairlie was one much better known to local people. The 160-foot-long paddle steamer *Pioneer* had been built in A & J Inglis' Partick shipyard for David MacBrayne Ltd in 1905 for service on the passenger and Royal Mail service to Islay from West Loch Tarbert. She continued on this run for many years, becoming one of the longest-serving and most popular of all MacBrayne's West Highland steamers. In 1939 she was replaced by the new motor vessel *Lochiel*. After short periods serving other island routes, and time laid up at Oban, *Pioneer* was purchased by the Admiralty for use as a second static laboratory and in March 1944 was moored in Fairlie Bay near *Dunvegan*. By the time of her purchase, however, a new aircraft carrier had just been launched for the Royal Navy and given the name HMS *Pioneer*. Like *Pandora*, *Pioneer* had to have a name change. Again the scientists of the Establishment must have had a say in that chosen, for it was with the name *Harbinger* that she was based at Fairlie – her new name cleverly reflecting the asdic's purpose of giving a sign of what is to come.

As with *Dunvegan*, high-voltage cables were laid to *Harbinger* from the shore to provide the considerable electrical power needed for the asdic devices under test. Her time at Fairlie was quite short, however, and in 1946 she too was towed down to Portland to continue in Admiralty service there as another floating laboratory. This role lasted until 1958 when *Harbinger* was sold for breaking up in Holland. Like *Dunvegan* and *Icewhale*, she was civilian manned during her two years moored at Fairlie, and again like the other two was not regarded as a Royal Navy ship and was not given an HMS title.

The MacBrayne paddle steamer *Pioneer* put in many years of service on the route between West Loch Tarbert and Islay.

With the new name *Harbinger*, the former *Pioneer* was based at Fairlie between 1944 and 1946. This photograph is probably taken after she was moved south to Portland.

The three merchant ships were primarily under the operational control of the Establishment's scientists and as such were not directly involved with the Royal Navy's ships and submarines. When new versions of asdic required to be tested against real submarines, the equipment had to be fitted to ships of the Royal Navy under the control of the Captain of the Establishment and the Flag Officer Western Approaches Command at Greenock. While some of the asdic developments under test were occasionally fitted to available destroyers and frigates, two smaller warships were attached to the Establishment on a near-permanent basis for the duration of the war. This continuity was very helpful to all concerned with the testing as it engendered a clear understanding between the scientists who had developed each piece of new equipment and the officers and men of the Navy who had to ensure it would really work in detecting U-boats in the North Atlantic and around Britain's coast.

Once the Navy was operationally satisfied with the equipment, it was the role of the officers based at Fairlie to oversee the fitting of the new asdics in the warships being constructed to hunt and destroy the U-boats. Even with very good co-operation, however, some barriers between the civilian scientists and the Royal Navy remained. One noted example was that each visit by a scientist or technician to a warship required to be approved by the Establishment's captain and a special pass issued. One of the conditions of issue was that the pass holder was forbidden from having any involvement in fighting an enemy ship should this take place while aboard the warship.

The smaller, and almost forgotten, of the two Royal Navy vessels based at Fairlie had the somewhat prosaic name of HMS *ML 199*. Only 112 feet long, she was one of the many hundreds of wooden-hulled coastal motor launches of the Fairmile B-class built during the Second World War and used for a wide range of purposes, both offensive and defensive. Conceived by a former car manufacturer, they were delivered from the Fairmile factory in Surrey to many different boatyards around Britain as six-part kits. *ML 199* was assembled at a yard located at Teddington on the River Thames and commissioned into the Royal Navy in December 1940 before coming north to Fairlie. A particular concern of the Admiralty at that time was the increasing use of British coastal waters by U-boats. In these shallower sea areas the type of asdic then fitted to the sloops and armed trawlers used to escort the inshore convoys was known to be less effective than in deeper water, reducing the chance of the U-boats being detected. The Establishment thus developed asdics specifically for small-ship shallow-water use and it was HMS *ML 199* that was used for the trials of these types. For most of her time at Fairlie she was under the command of a Royal Naval Volunteer Reserve Temporary Lieutenant. Along with almost all of the other wartime coastal motor launches, HMS *ML 199*'s value to the Navy ended when the war was over, and in August 1945 she was sold for civilian use.

The Fairmile B-class of motor launches had a top speed of 20 knots and a crew of sixteen. Fifteen of the boats were built on the Clyde at yards in Rosneath, Sandbank and Tarbert and a further twenty-nine at St Monans on the Firth of Forth. This photograph is of a boat similar to *ML 199*.

The second Royal Navy vessel and that best remembered in Fairlie today is HMS *Kingfisher*. Termed a patrol sloop (a type name later changed to corvette) and originally intended for coastal convoy escort duties as a slower and less costly alternative to the destroyer, *Kingfisher* was constructed at the Fairfield Shipyard at Govan on the Upper Clyde. From there she was launched without ceremony in February 1935. The lead ship of a class of nine all named after water-related birds, she was 243 feet in length and fitted with a single 4-inch gun and eight smaller anti-aircraft guns. She was also well equipped with both depth charge throwers and stern chutes and was capable of sailing at a speed of 20 knots. On commissioning in June 1935, *Kingfisher* joined the 1st Anti-Submarine Flotilla based at Portland where she became well known to the *Osprey* scientists working there. While at Portland she was one of the first Royal Navy warships fitted with an asdic transducer dome which when not required for searches could be retracted into a trunking fitted in the forward part of the keel. This greatly reduced the risk of damage to the dome in heavy seas.

After the outbreak of the war, *Kingfisher* continued to be based at Portland testing different developments of asdic. In May and June 1940, however, this work was interrupted when she became one of the many hundreds of vessels taking part in the Dunkirk evacuation, code-named Operation Dynamo. Between 30 May and 4 June, *Kingfisher* made five return trips to France, bringing to Britain some 885 British and French soldiers.

In August 1940 *Kingfisher* was damaged during the intensive bombing of Portland and its naval base. Repair work took some time but once complete she sailed north to join the relocated *Osprey* staff at Fairlie. Officially based at nearby Ardrossan (where the whole of the harbour was taken over by the Navy), *Kingfisher* was frequently seen throughout the war at her mooring in Fairlie Bay while being fitted with some new type of asdic for testing. This testing took place in the Firth of Clyde, up the west coast of Scotland, and occasionally out into the Atlantic, *Kingfisher* working with the Rothesay and Campbeltown-based Royal Navy submarines. She was fitted with numerous experimental and prototype transducers as well as different types and shapes of dome housing. One trial dome was believed to have been knocked off in the outer Firth by a whale or shark while another was lost in the North Channel during heavy weather. Large waves were always a problem for *Kingfisher* and her sister ships and it

HMS *Kingfisher* photographed prior to the Second World War with her original identification number P36. This was changed in 1940 to K70 and later to L70 – which can cause some confusion with photographs. The aft mast was removed at the start of the war. The depth-charge racks and side throwers can be seen at *Kingfisher*'s stern.

was her liveliness in such conditions that was the main reason for her being attached to *Osprey* as a trials ship rather than employed in the intended convoy protection role.

One of the most interesting of HMS *Kingfisher*'s experiments to Fairlie residents was when she used her 4-inch gun to test fire a new armour-piercing anti-submarine projectile known as Shark. This projectile did not contain any explosive charge but, being made of hardened steel, it was intended to simply punch a hole in a U-boat's outer and then inner casing. To determine whether the projectile would be lethal, a 19-foot-long steel structure was built to represent a section of a U-boat hull and then placed on the Fairlie shore at a location where it was fully submerged at high tide but dry at low tide. HMS *Kingfisher* was moored about 300 feet further offshore and fired her gun at the target once it was partially submerged. Analysis at low tide of the damage inflicted was judged to be well in excess of that needed to pierce a U-boat's pressure hull. Further testing of Shark was carried out on the underwater range. Together with HMS *Ambuscade*'s firing of the multiple Squid projectiles, Fairlie's wartime shore was not a very safe place for local residents to be in 1944.

Because of the mined hydrophone barrier put in place at the south-east end of Cumbrae, HMS *Kingfisher*'s route to and from Fairlie was around the north end of that island. The Clyde steamers which served Millport, Arran and Campbeltown from Fairlie during the war also had to follow this route. *Kingfisher*'s relationship with these steamers was not always a good one. It was a long-held custom of the sea that a merchant ship should not overtake a warship without the consent of the latter. It would seem that this courtesy was not always observed by the masters of the turbine steamers *Glen Sannox, Duchess of Argyll* and *Marchioness of Graham* when coming up astern of the slower-moving warship, leading on occasions to a few tersely worded signals to the steamer from *Kingfisher*'s captain. By another Establishment coincidence, when *Duchess of Argyll* reached the end of her Clyde service in 1952, she was acquired by the Admiralty and also taken to Portland for use as another floating asdic test laboratory. She was eventually broken up in 1969.

The much-loved Clyde turbine steamer *Glen Sannox* was built by William Denny at Dumbarton in 1925 for service on the Arran routes. She is shown here in her Second World War camouflage and was a familiar sight sailing to and from Fairlie Pier throughout the war.

During her time at Fairlie, HMS *Kingfisher* had six different commanding officers. It is an interesting demonstration of how the Royal Navy had to greatly expand its officer numbers as the war progressed that these changed in rank from a Royal Navy Lieutenant-Commander in 1940 to a Royal Naval Volunteer Reserve Temporary Lieutenant in 1945.

Kingfisher's crew of around sixty became well known in Fairlie as they came ashore for leave and changeovers. It was thus a great shock to the village, and to all of the Establishment staff, when six of her men were drowned after the boat taking them ashore sank in March 1944 during a storm. Their deaths greatly grieved everyone in Fairlie and

(*Left*) Wall plaque in Fairlie Parish Church commemorating the six members of the crew of HMS *Kingfisher* who were drowned off Fairlie. It was unveiled by the two survivors of the accident.

(*Above*) The report of the tragedy in the local Largs paper. Wartime censorship meant that there was no mention of the location of the accident or of HMS *Kingfisher*. Stoker Millington's name is wrongly spelt in the report.

are recorded on a memorial plaque on the east wall of Fairlie Parish
Church. This was dedicated in March 1946 at a special service attended
by *Kingfisher*'s crew and by many local people just before *Kingfisher*'s
final departure from Fairlie. A small vase beside the plaque is still filled
with fresh flowers for each Sunday service in Fairlie Church. The bod-
ies of the drowned men are interred in Commonwealth War Graves in
Largs Cemetery.

The graves in Largs Cemetery of the six members of HMS *Kingfisher*'s
crew who were drowned in March 1944.

Along with many other warships whose wartime service was over,
HMS *Kingfisher* was sold in 1947 for breaking-up. But her name and service are remembered not only in Fairlie and Largs. During the Second
World War the fundraising event Warship Week was introduced to
encourage cities, towns and even villages to raise money for a specific
ship and to then adopt her. Because of a local connection through
a crew member, *Kingfisher* was adopted by the town of Redditch in

REDDITCH WARSHIP WEEK

SOCIAL EVENTS

MILITARY BAND CONCERT

Arranged and performed by the members of the

CZECHOSLOVAK ARMY

IN THE DANILO CINEMA

(Kindly loaned free of charge by M. Dent Esq., Managing Director)

On SUNDAY, NOV. 16th, at 6.30 p.m.   Doors open 6 p.m.

All Balcony Seats are now booked, but Stalls are still available at 1/6

CONCERT

METHODIST SCHOOLROOM, ASTWOOD BANK

SATURDAY, NOVEMBER 15th

ALL STAR PROGRAMME.

DANCES

Washford Mills Recreation Room, Friday, November 14th. 2/6.

Headless Cross Memorial Hall, Tuesday, November 18th. 2/8.

Astwood Bank SS. Matthias and George Hall, Friday, Nov. 21st.

2/- Civilians, 1/6 Forces.

B.S.A. Piled Arms Club, Saturday, November 22nd. 3/-

SAVING STAMPS AS GIFTS AND PRIZES.

WHIST DRIVES

Washford Mills Recreation Room, Tuesday, Nov. 18th, 8 p.m., 1/-.

E.N.F.T. Canteen Hall, Studley, Saturday, Nov. 22nd, 7.30 p.m., 2/-.

FREE GIFTS OF SAVINGS STAMPS.

Have you got your Warship Badge?   The proceeds from the sale of these badges are to defray Warship Week expenses, publicity, etc.

IT IS OUR AIM TO SAVE
£120,000
DURING WARSHIP WEEK
TO BUY THE CORVETTE
H.M.S. "KINGFISHER"

"SAVE FOR YOUR SHARE"

See the grand collection of Naval Photographs at

THE SAVINGS CENTRE, CHURCH GREEN EAST.

Hours of opening 11 a.m. to 5 p.m. during

WARSHIP WEEK.

Advertisement for Redditch Warship Week to raise funds to the value of HMS *Kingfisher*.

Worcestershire after its residents and businesses contributed what in 2020 value would be £9.9 million. The warship later gave her name to a new shopping centre in the town, which was opened in 1976. A model of HMS *Kingfisher* was on display for some time in the Kingfisher Centre but unfortunately cannot now be traced.

In addition to the foregoing five ships it is known that a number of other vessels contributed to the work of the Establishment. No complete list can be found, but names which appear from time to time include *Lady of Avon, Plentitude* and *HDML 100*. The last would be one of the harbour defence motor launches again constructed in large numbers for the Navy, while the first two may have been some of the many private pleasure craft requisitioned by the Admiralty for war service. One quite frequent visitor to Fairlie was HMS *ML 472*, another of the Fairmile-type motor launches. Based at HMS *Seahawk* at Ardrishaig, she was – most unusually for such a small ship – fitted with a specially adapted version of Hedgehog as well as the latest asdic to examine the possibility of motor launches so equipped being used to hunt and sink U-boats in very shallow water. HMS *ML 472* was also used to test the ability of the X-craft submarines to escape detection during their secret trials in Loch Striven.

The renaming of the requisitioned merchant ships *Pandora* and *Pioneer* as *Icewhale* and *Harbinger* respectively was not the last of the asdic name associations of the Establishment. To transport men and equipment between Fairlie Pier and the ships moored in Fairlie Bay, the Admiralty provided at least one heavy-duty motor boat. At first nameless, this workboat was soon named *Spray* by the Establishment staff – the original name of the old coaster *Dunvegan*. At the end of the war the Admiralty handed *Spray* over to the owners of the Bay Street boatyard and under that name she could be seen for some years working in Fairlie Bay servicing moorings and towing yachts to and from the yard.

Chapter 7

LEISURE AND THE LOCALS

'our friends from the south'

Getting a sense of the relationship between the people of different nationalities and backgrounds who came to work at the Establishment during the course of the war and the local residents of Fairlie is not easy today. Even young children of the period are now in their late eighties or nineties, while none of those villagers who were employed there are still alive. Staff from England who returned down south after the war have also passed away. Only when reminiscences or recollections have been revealed to their children or other relatives can these be related – if still available. Even then, such was the level of secrecy enforced at the Establishment that few were able to talk or write about their experiences, or indeed even be aware of what others might be doing in the adjoining office, laboratory or workshop. Any improper words spoken in local pubs, such as the Village Inn in Bay Street opposite the yard, would soon be reported. The great emphasis on secrecy continued after the war ended. Not only were all records of the Establishment's research locked away in the National Archives until 1975, but as earlier noted, obituaries, biographies and other references to the scientists who came to the village rarely contain more than words such as 'Admiralty work at Fairlie' as their wartime activity.

Other than these references, the main sources for this part of the Establishment's history have been a very few personal communications and the archive of the local newspaper. Not surprisingly the content of the latter was very limited. Newspapers were subject to strict censorship and no reference to what was happening at the Establishment, or to any names, could be published. Not until the war was over did the word Portland ever appear in its Fairlie Notes column. Those who had come to the village were always referred to simply as 'our friends from the south'.

In considering the social interaction that took place between visitors and locals it must first be appreciated that the Establishment worked long hours. There was a war on, and the battle against the U-boats had to be won. Other than office staff, the working day for most staff started at 8 am and did not finish until 7 pm. Saturday mornings were worked by everyone and Sunday was the only full day off – except when the pressure to complete an experiment, test or report took precedence. After the initial billeting, many of the scientists and others who were not local to the area were able to rent houses and so allow their families to stay with them. When these rented homes were in Largs or West Kilbride, special buses were provided in the morning and evening from and to these neighbouring towns. Thus the opportunities for socialising with the Fairlie villagers were always somewhat limited. As one young technical officer later wrote about his time in Fairlie: 'we were isolated in a sense, which meant a little community of scientists – we didn't mix much with the natives'.

Because of this sense of isolation – another former Portland scientist described Fairlie as being 'the back of beyond' – the Establishment staff developed their own interests either collectively or as individuals or small groups. Bicycles were acquired by many. The roads to West Kilbride and Largs were quiet, with the main vehicles other than buses and lorries being military – including occasional columns of tanks heading to Largs for exercises. Cycling to and from work, especially during summer, became commonplace. Others took up or continued hill walking and climbing. There was still a regular steamer service between Fairlie and the island of Arran and it was possible over a weekend to have a full day climbing among the high peaks. So much

Four of the Establishment's scientists enjoying a game of cards
during their lunch break.

did some of the young scientists enjoy this activity that they could
be found during their half-hour lunch break practising their skills on
the near-vertical rock face of Craig Hill located conveniently close to
the Establishment. A snooker table was available in the Fairlieburne
officers' mess and was frequently used by the scientists when invited.
Others preferred a game of cards: bridge was particularly popular as it
was seen as an easy way of relaxing the brain after a full day of complex
calculations.

During the summer months, tennis was popular, the Establishment
staff taking over and maintaining two of the village courts. A cricket
match arranged between the local and the visiting schoolboys was not
a success. Cricket and bowling at stumps were not common in prewar
Fairlie but, as in most seaside communities, there was considerable
expertise among the local children in throwing stones with some accuracy at tin cans floating in the sea. Not surprisingly the English boys

Moshé Feldenkrais taught judo and self-defence in Fairlie Primary School after his day doing asdic research work. While at Fairlie he also wrote the book *Practical Unarmed Combat*.

strongly objected to the transfer of this somewhat alarming approach to aiming a cricket ball, and no further cricket matches between the two groups are noted. Relationships between the nationalities were soon repaired, however, with ice cream being served on public holidays from the Establishment's canteen. For some local children this was their first taste of what at the time was a great luxury, given the severe restrictions of wartime food rationing.

A more unusual activity introduced to the village was judo. The Ukrainian-born scientist Moshé Feldenkrais learned this self-defence skill during his early years in Palestine and by the time he came to Fairlie, he had attained rare and prestigious black-belt status. Soon he was encouraging his colleagues to take up the sport, first giving demonstrations in their homes and later in the village school when he persuaded the headmaster to allow him to run classes in the evening. After finishing his day's research work, Feldenkrais would go to the school, clear away the classroom furniture, carry heavy floor mats up from the school cellar, and then do the reverse after demonstrations and teaching. A condition of the school's use was that local people could join his classes, although no mention has been found of any taking up the offer.

More collectively, many of the Establishment's staff formed an entertainment section known as The Supersonics (no clue there for German spies!). Over three evenings in December 1941 a concert was presented in Fairlie Village Hall with a programme of vocal and instrument solos, duets and a choir. All proceeds were given to the

Naval Comfort Fund. The concerts were noted in the local paper as being 'greatly appreciated' by the audiences of both villagers and Establishment staff. The choir, which met weekly, sang to an invited audience at the nearby Kelburn Castle each Christmas. Another part of The Supersonics formed a dance band called The Serenaders which was much in demand throughout the local area.

In October 1942 the local paper was telling its Fairlie readers: 'our friends from the south who have made their wartime homes within our gates are livening things up by forming a dramatic club'. Rehearsals were held after work in the Village Hall, sometimes going on to near midnight. The club's first play – *I Killed the Count* – was produced by January 1943 and was presented first in Fairlie and later in the Dunn Memorial Hall in Largs. This was followed in March 1944 by *The Middle Watch*, appropriately a comedy about a warship. As well as being presented in Largs, this play went on tour, being seen by audiences in West Kilbride and at HMS *Osprey* in Dunoon. *The Fourth Wall* was performed in January 1945, and finally in June 1945, *French Without Tears*, a production acclaimed by the local paper and the audience as 'The Supersonics' crowning success'.

The cast of the play *The Middle Watch*, presented at Fairlie in March 1944. Finding Royal Navy uniforms for the actors would not have been difficult.

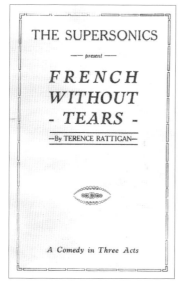
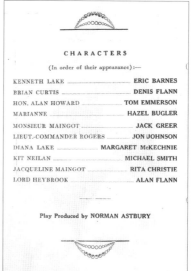

THE SUPERSONICS

— present —

FRENCH
WITHOUT
- TEARS -

—By TERENCE RATTIGAN—

A Comedy in Three Acts

CHARACTERS

(In order of their appearance):—

KENNETH LAKE	ERIC BARNES
BRIAN CURTIS	DENIS FLANN
HON. ALAN HOWARD	TOM EMMERSON
MARIANNE	HAZEL BUGLER
MONSIEUR MAINGOT	JACK GREER
LIEUT.-COMMANDER ROGERS	JON UOHNSON
DIANA LAKE	MARGARET McKECHNIE
KIT NEILAN	MICHAEL SMITH
JACQUELINE MAINGOT	RITA CHRISTIE
LORD HEYBROOK	ALAN FLANN

Play Produced by NORMAN ASTBURY

The programme and cast list for The Supersonics' last production. Both Tom Emmerson and the producer Norman Astbury were scientists, but the positions of the other members of the cast are not known. Tickets for The Supersonics productions were available at the Fairlie Pier Station kiosk and in the local post office.

A Supersonics Club dinner dance for Establishment staff and other guests was held in the Marine Hotel in Largs in February 1943. Over 100 attended with the toast 'The Royal Navy' being proposed by Largs physician Dr Roberts and responded to by Commander Binnie. Hogmanay was a new experience for most of the Royal Navy and former Portland staff. In December 1943 the local paper was reporting 'our friends from south of the border (again no mention of Portland) now resident with us showed how they celebrate Christmas. It is up to us to return the compliment at Ne'er Day'.

Raising funds for the war effort was a continuous activity through-out Great Britain. In Fairlie this included sales of work, garden fetes and whist drives, with money being given to national appeals such as 'Wings for Victory' and 'Warship Week'. As its contribution to Warship Week, Fairlie adopted HMS *Tuscarora*, a former steam yacht

Second World War Savings Posters.

The luxury steam yacht *Tuscarora* served as HMS *Tuscarora* at Campbeltown during the Second World War. She was built by Scotts at Greenock in 1897 and was one of the finest of the classic steam yachts by which successful businessmen of the time demonstrated their wealth. After the war she had a series of Greek owners as a cargo vessel before foundering in Middle Eastern waters in 1968.

built for a member of the Clark thread-making family and requisitioned by the Royal Navy at the start of the Second World War. HMS *Tuscarora* was based at HMS *Nimrod* in Campbeltown where she was one of the warships used to train naval ratings in the operation of asdic after their introductory classes at Dunoon. 'Comforts' such as jerseys, socks and hats were knitted by the Fairlie ladies and regularly sent to Campbeltown. In all these activities, Establishment staff participated as their work allowed, sometimes helping out with equipment. In June 1944 a united evening service of the village's two churches – St Margaret's and St Paul's – was held at the latter with the proceedings

An Establishment wedding. The groom is the scientist Eric Alexander and the bride is Muriel McKinnon, one of the technical staff. The best man (far right) is believed to be another scientist, George Hodsman.

being amplified and relayed outside to other worshippers using acoustic equipment provided by the Establishment; it is believed to be the very first such broadcast from a local place of worship.

It has not been easy to obtain information about more personal relationships between the incomers and the residents of Fairlie. It is believed that such relationships did develop, with weddings taking place either during or just after the war ended. Unfortunately, no records of such marriages at either of the two Fairlie churches have been found. At least one wedding between Establishment staff did take place outside of the village, however. A photograph provided to the author by a Weymouth family shows the bridal party for a wedding ceremony held in a Glasgow church in October 1944.

It is difficult today to gain any greater insight into the social interaction that must have taken place at Fairlie during the years the village was host to HM Anti-Submarine Experimental Establishment. Every local resident, whether living in the village throughout the war or coming home on leave from their own military service, would have come into some contact with a group of people – Royal Navy officers and scientists – in most cases very different in background from themselves. The visitors would use local shops, walk the local roads and in many cases lodge with local residents. What did Fairlie folk think of their 'friends' from the south? Is there some old diary or notebook still waiting to be discovered?

Chapter 8

TIME TO GO HOME

'even if they did not know it at the time'

By the beginning of 1945 it was clear that Germany was going to be defeated and that the war in Europe would soon be over. While the research and experimental work of the Establishment continued – even accelerated with the discovery of the revolutionary high underwater speed U-boats and the challenge these would present for future anti-submarine warfare – plans were being made to return HMS *Osprey* to Portland. The Clyde had served *Osprey* well since its sudden arrival at the end of 1940, but both the Royal Navy and the former Portland staff simply wanted to return to their historic south-coast base, and of course to their own homes. For others of the 1945 staff, there were different circumstances. Those who had been recruited as Temporary Experimental Officers had come from all over Britain, and from overseas, and most wished to go back home. Fairlie, some would have agreed, might be a pleasant place to live, but not one with the attractions of a city or large town. Many of the young scientists also wished to pursue careers outwith the Admiralty and felt that having made their contribution to winning the war it was time to move on. With the final surrender of Germany approaching, the Establishment began the release of its temporary staff.

So far as is known, the surrender of Germany and VE Day on 8 May 1945 were not major events for the Establishment. The war with Japan continued and both the scientists and the naval officers were well aware that Royal Navy ships and submarines were still under attack. The only noted marking of the day was the brief display of flags from bow to top of mast to stern by the warships then in Fairlie Bay, although no doubt all of the staff took great satisfaction a couple of days later on hearing that the first of the German U-boats to surrender had been taken into Portland Harbour. After the surrender of the U-boats was complete and all the known boats accounted for, the Royal Navy took *U-1023* on a tour of British west-coast ports for visits by the public. Open days were held on the Clyde at Rothesay, Greenock and Glasgow – but not at the still-secret Fairlie!

The surrender of Japan on 15 August allowed everyone at the Establishment to finally relax. At the announcement that hostilities were over, the local paper reported that all the Royal Navy ships in Fairlie Bay 'turned night into day' with a brilliant display of searchlights, rockets and flares, while sirens and ships' bells 'sounded continually'.

It was at this time that some of the secrecy surrounding His Majesty's Anti-Submarine Experimental Establishment could be very slightly lifted with a photograph being taken of all who were then working there. This 'family photo' was taken in the forecourt of the nearby bus garage at the north end of the village and shows some 280 people. Royal Navy officers and the senior scientists are seated in the centre of the front row, with diminishing seniority moving sideways and upwards from there until the back row of what is likely to comprise the non-technical staff. The number of women in the photograph is interesting. These included scientists, technical and secretarial staff, and those engaged for more domestic duties. Unfortunately, despite the photograph being reproduced in the Fairlie local paper, in Weymouth, and elsewhere, hardly any names have been put to those placed in the various rows of men and women.

With the organisation of the return to Portland underway and the Establishment staff starting to disperse, Fairlie's last Royal Navy Captain, Robert Dendy, took the opportunity to speak at a Thanksgiving Savings Week public meeting held in Fairlie Village Hall on 5 October. During

The left half of the July 1945 photograph of the Establishment staff. The eleven Royal Navy officers on the right side of this photograph are shown in greater detail on page 91.

The right half of the July 1945 photograph of the Establishment staff. Superintending Scientist Jock Anderson is seated first from the left on the second row. Note the three Admiralty policemen on the right side of the top row. The four Royal Navy sailors in the middle of that row would include Captain Dendy's coxswain.

his informal address he expressed his most sincere thanks to the people of Fairlie for all of the support and assistance afforded by them to the Establishment and the Royal Navy throughout the war. He also announced that in the following week there would be an opportunity for local people to go aboard and see round both HMS *Kingfisher* and HMS *ML 199*. This invitation was widely accepted and on 13 October a steady stream of Fairlie folk were ferried by launch to and from the two warships. HMS *Kingfisher* was by then fully illuminated each night at her mooring and was reported as 'making a pleasing spectacle in Fairlie Bay'.

On 4 December the ship's company of HMS *Kingfisher* held a dance at Barrfields Pavilion in Largs. Late buses were provided to Fairlie and Ardrossan, with all proceeds of the evening going to charity. On 17 December The Supersonics gave their last performance, and on Hogmanay the Establishment staff held their final dinner dance in the Marine Hotel in Largs. At the dinner a toast 'to our Scottish friends' was proposed by the Establishment's senior scientist Jock Anderson. This was responded to by Mr William Hirst of Fairlie House, the Commandant of the by then disbanded Fairlie Home Guard. Sadly, one person not present at any of these events was Fairlie's world renowned yacht designer and builder William Fife, who had passed away in August 1944 at the age of 87.

As 1945 turned into 1946, more and more of Fairlie's 'English friends of the last six years' left the Establishment and the village. Plans to move the remainder, together with families, pets and possessions, were finalised. The Establishment's apparatus and equipment was also crated up and made ready for transport south by train. On Friday 3 February, Captain Dendy, Superintendent Anderson and other senior staff of the Establishment hosted a farewell social in Barrfields to mark the occasion of their departure from Fairlie. Some 700 invited guests attended.

Captain Dendy again gave a short speech. In this he advised the guests that a large number of the U-boat sinkings during the recent war were directly attributable to the efforts of the staff at Fairlie and the surrounding district 'who had, in countless ways, helped the Establishment to do its work'. In particular he praised the housewives of the village 'who had so successfully shared their homes and their kitchens with the invaders from the south'. Captain Dendy concluded by expressing his personal regret that it had become necessary to leave Fairlie, adding 'if every community was run on the lines on which Fairlie was run, the country would be a much better place to live in'. Such appreciation was echoed by Superintendent Anderson, who in a short speech informed the guests that 'without the research carried out at Fairlie, the Battle of the Atlantic, and indeed the German war, could not have been won'. Even if not completely true, it was the first public statement of the vital importance of Fairlie's secret war.

Major David Thorburn, a retired army officer living at Creich House – another of Fairlie's large seashore mansions – then responded on behalf of the people of Fairlie. They were all very proud, he said, to have helped in the destruction of so many U-boats – 'even if they did not know it at the time'. He believed that Fairlie would undoubtedly miss the Establishment and the contribution of the visitors to the wartime social life of the village. On behalf of all the local people, he 'wished good luck to all those who were returning south'.

The day of the Establishment's final departure from Fairlie was Thursday 28 February 1946. A special train of seven coaches and four luggage vans was provided for the long journey south to Portland. This left from Largs Station at 3.10 that afternoon. Some 134 people were aboard – staff, partners and children, plus pets, prams and much more – together with all the Establishment's documents and plans. As the train came out of the Fairlie Tunnel and steamed slowly southwards through Fairlie Station, its passengers were greeted by a large crowd of villagers who, many with tears in their eyes, waved a last goodbye. His Majesty's Anti-Submarine Experimental Establishment's very secret time at Fairlie was over.

Chapter 9

POSTSCRIPT

'to better understand the water environment'

The previous chapters have told the story of HM Anti-Submarine Experimental Establishment Fairlie and the work carried out there during the Second World War on the development of underwater acoustics, asdic and ahead-throwing weapons. But many other anti-submarine developments also contributed to Britain's battle against the U-boats and it is appropriate that some mention be made of these. It is also of interest to look briefly at post-Second World War advances in underwater warfare and how these followed on from the research undertaken at the Establishment. And finally, what of the village of Fairlie today?

In the opening months of the Second World War, the introduction of the convoy system was an early measure taken by the Admiralty to contain the U-boat attacks. This had been shown to be effective in the First World War and involved the grouping of individual merchant ships into a single fleet – sometimes comprising over 100 vessels – and providing warships to defend the group. The warships, mainly asdic-equipped frigates and corvettes, patrolled around the perimeter of the convoy to provide some warning of the presence of a submerged U-boat. If an asdic echo was confirmed as likely to be from a U-boat, the escorts would mount a depth-charge attack. The main intention of such attacks was to keep the U-boat – or increasingly as the war progressed groups of U-boats which were referred to as wolf packs – submerged while the convoy moved on. It was hoped these measures would allow most of the merchant ships to continue their voyage safely, as once submerged a U-boat was generally unable to keep up with even the slowest moving convoys. The convoy system was only effective, however, if there were enough escort vessels to protect the ships. This took time to achieve and, as described in Chapter 3, many convoys suffered significant losses in the early years of the war.

As more and better equipped warships did become available, the convoy escorts were supported by special hunting groups of faster anti-submarine frigates. The prime role of these groups was an active or offensive one – the destruction of any U-boats found – as against the passive or defensive role of the slower escorts whose first duty was to ensure the safe passage of the merchant ships. Equipped with the latest types of asdic, and later the ahead-throwing weapons Hedgehog or Squid, such hunter-killer groups were very effective.

Asdic was of course only of use for the detection of a submerged U-boat, and only when the U-boat was submerged within a mile or so of the convoy. It provided no warning against the surfaced U-boat. Initially any spotting of a U-boat on the surface was reliant on the good vision of the escort's lookouts, a near impossible task in bad weather, or at night when most attacks took place. Very often the first indication a convoy had of a U-boat attack was the explosion of a torpedo against one of its ships. Where had the attack come from, and which ship would be sunk next? Not until the U-boat submerged was asdic of any help.

The first breakthrough in detecting a surfaced U-boat came with the Admiralty's ability to intercept the high-frequency radio messages sent by the submarine to the German Navy Command. By triangulating the bearing of the transmitted signal from different shore receivers, a good indication was obtained of the U-boat's location. This provided the convoy with some warning of its presence and the possibility of an attack. But the most important use of radio intercepts came in May 1941 with the very secret capture of a U-boat with its Enigma coding machine and codebooks intact. After the code was broken at Bletchley

Park it became possible for the Admiralty to read the radio communications between the German Navy Command and the operational U-boats. As attacks on convoys were more successful when mounted by a group of boats, it was standard German Navy practice that once a convoy had been sighted by a U-boat or a long-range aircraft, the spotter would radio the position to U-boat headquarters, which in turn would instruct other U-boats to move to the location for a wolf pack attack. The Admiralty's interception and decoding of these messages enabled the commander of the convoy's escort to be advised of that location and then alter the convoy's course to try and avoid the gathering U-boats. If this was not possible, the escorting warships would be put on full alert, with the asdic operators and the depth-charge crews ready to start the counter-attack. If any support groups were available in the area these would be directed to where the U-boats were gathering, either to disrupt the group or, more hopefully, sink some of them.

The most important Second World War development in the detection of a surfaced U-boat was the introduction of radar and its fitting to the Royal Navy's anti-submarine warships. Radar enabled a warship to find a surfaced U-boat at night or in poor visibility, even when some miles away. The U-boat could then be attacked by the warship's guns. Once an attack started, or the attacking warship was spotted, the U-boat usually crash-dived to rapidly submerge. Asdic then took over the search. As an increasing number of escort vessels were fitted with both radar and the latest types of asdic, the number of ships lost from torpedo attack when part of a convoy steadily reduced, while the number of U-boats sunk steadily increased. During 1941 twenty-five U-boats were sunk directly by Royal Navy warships; during 1944 the total rose to sixty-four.

The anti-submarine warships of the Second World War were quite limited in the extent of the sea's area they could search, even with the best radar and the best asdic. This limitation was removed when the use of aircraft was introduced for hunting the U-boats. For close support of convoys these could be flown from escort aircraft carriers and

An Atlantic convoy viewed from the V-class destroyer HMS *Vanoc*. Built
in 1917 at John Brown's Clydebank shipyard, in March 1941 she depth-
charged and sank *U-100* south-east of Iceland. The submarine had been
identified on the surface by *Vanoc*'s recently fitted radar. The two rails of
depth charges shown on *Vanoc*'s stern await priming.

merchant ship conversions, but it was the long-range aircraft operating
from shore bases in Britain, Canada and Iceland that were the main
searchers. The Germans had for some time used long-range shore-
based aircraft to locate a convoy and then by radio direct any U-boats
in the vicinity to its position. Now the Royal Air Force could reverse
that role and if a surfaced U-boat was found by an aircraft, it could
direct any nearby Royal Navy or other Allied warships to its position.

But the aircraft could go further. With planes like the Catalina and
Sunderland flying boats, the Fleet Air Arm Swordfish and the powerful
Liberator bomber, a U-boat found on the surface could be vigorously
attacked. Heavy cannon and later rocket firing, and the dropping
of bombs, rendered surface movement by the U-boats extremely
hazardous. Once the submarine crash-dived, the plane could drop
shallow-setting depth charges with some accuracy – based on the trajectory tests at Fairlie's underwater range. Towards the end of the war,

136

aircraft were also used to deploy what are now known as sonobuoys. These were expendable battery-powered hydrophones dropped into the sea to listen for U-boat noise. Any sound heard was then transmitted by radio to the overflying aircraft or to a nearby warship to assist a subsequent attack.

From official figures published after the end of the Second World War, it is believed that 206 U-boats were sunk by Royal Navy warships and 211 by British land-based and carrier-based aircraft. A further 30 are recorded as being sunk by a joint action of British ships and aircraft. In stating this near equality, however, it should be noted that all of the U-boats sunk by aircraft were on or very close to the surface, whereas the great majority of those sunk by warships were submerged, often at some considerable depth, and thus in effect were killed by asdic.

Despite a total of 785 U-boats being destroyed one way or another during the Second World War, and the postwar assertion of Churchill that the U-boats had been 'conquered', the reality of the anti-submarine battles is that the Royal Navy did not defeat the U-boats. Even in the last days of the war, there were still fifty-seven of them at sea actively seeking and attacking British and allied ships, and in doing so tying down some 400 or so allied warships and twice as many aircraft. As Captain Roskill, the Royal Navy's official Second World War historian, concluded after the war was over, 'we never gained a firm and final mastery over the U-boats'.

The role of the U-boat in the Second World War, as in the First World War, was to try to force Britain into surrender, or at least sue for a peace, by preventing enough supplies of food, raw materials and oil from reaching the island nation. While nearly doing so – particularly in 1942 – in this the U-boat failed. It was thus the defeat of the objective of the U-boats that was the Royal Navy's victory, and it was to this victory that the Establishment's work contributed so greatly.

The return of HMS *Osprey* to Portland in 1946 was by no means the end of the struggle for supremacy between the submarine and those who hunt the submarine. At Germany's surrender, the victors raced to the wartime U-boat bases at Kiel and Hamburg to discover the secrets of the reported high-submerged-speed, deep-diving submarine, which their navies had not so far encountered. What they found from their inspections and later testing caused great concern. Designed as a true submarine and not just as a submersible boat, the Type XXI was able to move more quickly and more quietly underwater than any other submarine then in existence, and could stay submerged for up to eleven days at a time. The outer hull was fully streamlined and free of all of the protrusions which caused resistance and turbulence. Together with powerful diesel engines, larger batteries and very efficient electric motors, the new profile resulted in a maximum surfaced speed of just over 15 knots and a maximum submerged speed of 18 knots – around 11 knots greater than the fastest of any of the earlier types of submarine. Much improved structural strength resulted in a probable maximum diving depth of over 800 feet.

Of greatest interest to the Fairlie scientists who were sent to examine the U-boats was the streamlined form of the Type XXI boat and its very small acoustic signature, confirming the findings of their experiments with HMS *Seraph*. Also discovered within the larger submarine was an echo chamber which was equipped with sophisticated active and passive detectors able to track multiple targets simultaneously – underwater acoustic developments which the scientists of the Establishment had only just started work on. The apparent acoustic invisibility of the smaller Type XXIII coastal U-boats was also a surprise.

It was indeed fortunate for Britain that the war was over before more than a handful of the new generation of U-boats became operational, and fortunate also that throughout the Second World War the Royal Navy had only to counter submarines with a very small underwater speed and a very limited underwater endurance. As the Royal Navy's Flag Officer Submarines reported to the Admiralty in July 1945, 'we stand on the threshold of very considerable technical development and thus the submarine of the future may differ profoundly from the submersibles of the present and past'.

The realisation by the British, French, American and Russian experts who pored over the captured Type XXI boats that their navies had no ready technical and operational answers to fighting such a submarine was very alarming. The immediate result was a massive acceleration in the postwar development of both submarine and anti-submarine measures necessary to find and destroy them. As they had before the Second World War, during the war and after 1945, the scientists of HMS *Osprey* and its successor establishments continued to be at the forefront of the necessary research.

In 1955 nuclear energy powered a submarine underwater for the first time. Unlike a diesel engine, a nuclear reactor does not require an external air supply and, with internal air cleaning, a submarine so powered can remain submerged for many weeks. This capability was fully demonstrated by the United States Navy's USS *Nautilus* when she travelled right round the world at a speed of 25 knots without surfacing. The nuclear age also introduced a new role for the submarine – that of providing a mobile and elusive delivery platform for airborne missiles. As the range and destructive power of these missiles increased, the submarine became the deterrent of choice for the main nuclear powers. Larger and larger submarines entered service. Today these boats are able to travel at high, but still very secret, underwater speeds, and can also remain still, and almost silent, with very small acoustic profiles, for many weeks anywhere in the world's oceans. There they just sit, waiting, listening intently to their array of passive sonars for a warning of any hunter.

The Royal Navy's all-nuclear fleet of submarines is today based at Faslane on the Gare Loch, also the home of the shore base HMS *Neptune*. Among the base's facilities is a state-of-the-art sonar training facility. Appropriately, and probably unknown to those who use it, the facility is sited very close to that of the Shandon establishment where much of the pioneering research on underwater acoustics – a science now called hydroacoustics – took place a century ago.

One of the Royal Navy's Vanguard-class intercontinental ballistic missile submarines. Some of the many different passive and active acoustic sensors with which these boats are equipped are visible on the side panels. Underwater speeds are believed to be at least 25 knots and maximum diving depths may be around 2,000 feet. The V-class boats will be replaced by the new Dreadnought class.

The Royal Navy's new Astute-class attack submarines are intended to provide anti-submarine protection to both Royal Navy surface ships and submarines. Guided torpedoes are believed to have a range of up to 30 miles. They also have the capability to launch missile attacks on land targets and undertake stealth and surveillance missions. Their active and passive sonar systems – some contained within the raised casings visible at the bow and stern, and others towed behind the boat as multi-sensor arrays – are among the most advanced in the world.

The submarine's role of deterrence can only remain credible if the submarine cannot be found when it goes on its mission and so cannot be neutralised. Thus new anti-submarine techniques and weaponry have had to be developed to try to locate, track and if necessary destroy the submarine. Asdic, now always referred to as sonar, has undergone advances which the Second World War scientists at Fairlie could only have dreamed about. Using both active and passive techniques able to search around the hunter in three dimensions, multiple underwater objects can be detected at distances of many hundreds of miles. The acoustic signals received can be very rapidly analysed by powerful on-board computers to identify not only the presence of a submarine but, using an acoustic profile library, also its type and even its name. Multiple targets can be tracked, and if ordered, new forms of homing torpedoes and other underwater weapons can then be launched. Should an enemy submarine attempt an attack by torpedo, the modern warship can quickly identify that threat and release multiple acoustic decoys with a sonar profile similar to that of the ship under attack.

Acoustic sensing, whether in active or passive modes – and still to a great extent the interpretation of underwater sound by a skilled operator – remains the predominant means of locating a submarine. In response, the submarine designer continues to put much effort into making today's boats as near acoustically invisible as possible. Sound-absorbent hull coverings, minimising and indeed removing all internal sources of noise, very silent propellers, and movement of the submarine through the water without using a rotating propeller, for example by low-turbulence water pump jets, are just some of the developments in use or being researched by those favouring the submarine. So, again in turn, the drive for acoustic invisibility has resulted in the anti-submarine researchers developing ways to locate a submerged submarine which do not involve sound. Today trials go on with heat, pressure, electro-magnetic, turbulence and other forms of sensor able to detect the minute changes in the physical properties of the sea caused by the presence or movement of a submarine.

Not all of today's submarines are nuclear powered or are intended to launch nuclear missiles. Much less costly to construct and operate are ones propelled underwater by air-independent, very silent diesel-electric or fuel-cell motors. As governments around the world have come to appreciate the versatility of the true submarine, some forty countries now include two or more non-nuclear boats in their naval forces. They can undertake a wide range of offensive and defensive tasks. They can attack an enemy by the firing of torpedoes and missiles and can carry manned and unmanned 'mini-subs' and underwater drones for covert operations. Work on developing a fully unmanned, remotely controlled submarine proceeds. With the ocean floor now criss-crossed by myriad pipelines and power and telecommunication cables, the use of such boats to sever these sub-sea arteries is likely to cause an island nation some difficulty. And doing so will be much easier than attacking convoys of merchant ships.

The contest between the submarine and those wishing to neutralise its offensive potential continues. It is a contest which both protagonists must always strive to win. In 2019 the Royal Navy formally stated that 'the attack submarine remains the greatest single danger to naval operations' and that 'anti-submarine warfare is fundamental to UK security'. A new programme of research was initiated into how that attack potential can be minimised, and equally for its own submarines, how it can be maximised. Among the tasks identified as being of high priority was 'to better understand the water environment'. How familiar that call would have been to the Fairlie scientists!

As today's Royal Navy submarines make their way through the waters of the Firth of Clyde to and from their Gare Loch base, what of Fairlie? The removal to Portland of all the equipment the Admiralty wished to retain was completed during 1947, and the Bay Street boatyard which had been occupied by the Establishment since October 1940 was returned to its owner. William Fife (III) did not marry and, after his death in 1944, it was his nephew Robert Balderstone Fife who took ownership of the yard. Balderstone Fife had worked with his uncle at Fairlie for many years before the war and had been made a partner in the world-famous business. Not perhaps such an imaginative yacht designer as the three William Fifes, his main role under his uncle had been organising and supervising the work being carried out in the Bay Street yard, particularly when William was away from Fairlie meeting prospective clients.

With the yard's wartime requisition and the death of his uncle, Balderstone Fife appears to have lost interest in building yachts and within a short time of the Bay Street yard being returned to him by the Admiralty he sold the business and the property. Soon after, it was acquired by the Fairlie Yacht Slip Company. For some years this local concern had occupied a small boatyard on the north side of Fairlie Pier and, while never competing with Fife in terms of yacht design, did a steady trade in the building and repair of a wide variety of wooden boats. During the Second World War it was kept fully occupied working on the smaller Admiralty-owned and requisitioned craft as well as civilian vessels. It was an obvious choice to take over the historic Bay Street site.

The return of the shore on the west side of Bay Street to a working boatyard was not welcomed by all in Fairlie. The Fife yard had always developed somewhat haphazardly in terms of its various sheds and other structures and its overall external appearance had not been helped by the wartime additions. There were thus a number of Fairlie residents who suggested that with the Royal Navy's departure from the village the opportunity should be taken to demolish the buildings, clear the site and 'let Fairlie have back the open foreshore that nature intended'. But these pleas were ignored and the Yacht Slip Company set about refurbishing its new acquisition. This work was greatly assisted by the considerable improvements made to the former Fife yard by the Admiralty, including the provision of electricity and the substantial drawing office and workshop facilities. Generally the owners of requisitioned property were not financially compensated by the government at the end of the war if the property was returned in its previous condition, so with the yard's facilities being in a much better state than they were at the end of 1940 it is unlikely that the new occupant received a great sum of money.

What the Yacht Slip Company did get from the Admiralty as a form of compensation were orders for the construction of some minor Royal Navy vessels, and other Admiralty small craft such as the barges of the Royal Yacht HMS *Britannia*. Thus seven 110-foot-long inshore mine-sweepers were built at the Bay Street yard and delivered to the Navy between 1953 and 1958. They were a part of the order for ninety-three of the mainly wooden HAM-class sweepers which were to be supplied by numerous boatyards located throughout Britain in response to a concern that the Soviet Union might use mines to blockade Britain's ports. All of these small warships were named after English villages with a name ending in 'ham'. As the threat of widespread mining reduced during the 1960s, however, few of the class lasted long in Royal Navy

Named after a small village in Kent, the inshore minesweeper HMS *Cobham* was launched from the Bay Street yard on 14 May 1953. After mainly serving in Hong Kong she was broken up in 1966. The workboat in the foreground is thought to be *Spray*, left behind by the Admiralty after the Establishment's return to Portland. Fairlie Pier and the Pier Station are in the background.

service and most were sold off for commercial or private use. One of the Fairlie-built boats, HMS *Ludham*, was bought by the new University of Strathclyde in 1967 and converted into a hydrographic survey vessel. As such she was engaged in studies for a proposed and very controversial iron ore terminal to be sited in the deep waters of Fairlie Bay just a short distance from her birthplace.

In addition to boat building, the postwar Fairlie yard was kept busy with repair work and by operating and maintaining the many yacht moorings in Fairlie Bay. At one point in the 1950s nearly 200 people were employed, but with traditional wooden yachts being rapidly replaced by factory-built fibreglass ones, orders declined. In 1985 the

As well as the Royal Navy minesweepers, Fairlie Yacht Slip built wooden yachts and fishing boats. The *Silver Lining* (shown being launched) and her sister *Silver Fern* were constructed in 1950 and were traditional-style Clyde ring netters which worked as a pair to catch herring. The registration BA indicates Ballantrae as the home port although in practice the two boats were based further up the Ayrshire coast at Maidens.

The Bay Street yard just before the site was cleared. All of the buildings
visible once formed part of the Establishment.

historic yard finally closed. Today the site where so many fine yachts
were built by the three William Fifes, and where so much was done by
the Establishment to help win the Second World War, is occupied by
the ubiquitous private housing.

But Fairlie's role in anti-submarine warfare did not end with the
return of the Establishment to Portland. In the early 1950s there was
growing concern about a possible conflict with the Soviet Union, and
the Clyde with its ready access to the Atlantic and North America was
identified as a major base for NATO warships. Many new mooring
buoys were put in place, some such as those in Largs Bay and Rothesay
Bay able to take the largest aircraft carriers. To install and maintain
the moorings, what was described as a NATO mooring and support
depot was constructed on reclaimed land to the north of Fairlie Pier.
It included very large sheds, railway access and a deep-water jetty.
Although some suggest that it was built as an emergency base for
United States nuclear submarines, it is believed that the depot was

originally developed to maintain a physical barrier intended to prevent Soviet submarines entering the Clyde. The barrier planned for the Hunterston Channel included both nets in the deeper water and a line of steel piles extending seawards across the Southannan Sands to low water mark. Unlike the net booms placed between Gourock and Dunoon during both the First and Second World Wars, however, the Hunterston barrier was to have no opening section. While the piles were put in across the intertidal area (and in later years removed), there is no evidence that the nets were ever deployed.

For local people the most obvious use of the Fairlie depot before its closure in 1996 was indeed the laying and servicing of warship moorings at locations throughout the west of Scotland. Examples of the anchors used for the mooring buoys are today displayed along the footpath between Fairlie and Largs. Much less obvious and not generally known, however, was the depot's role in the installation of the lines of hydrophones laid on the seabed around the UK coast as part of NATO's Sound Surveillance System. A modern and much more sophisticated version of the passive listening devices of the First and Second World Wars, SOSUS was – and an updated version still is – widely used to detect the movement of submarines, record their acoustic profile, and if any threat is perceived, direct anti-submarine forces to their location. As with the Establishment's wartime work, this activity was undertaken in the greatest secrecy.

With the 1970s rationalisation of military bases, the Fairlie depot closed and its work transferred elsewhere. The site was then sold and redeveloped as a commercial boatyard. The associated jetty with its water depth of 33 feet is still in use and is occasionally visited by Royal Navy and other NATO warships. There is a much larger jetty to the south, almost opposite the former Establishment site. This was opened in 1979 to facilitate the unloading of iron ore and coal for the Lanarkshire steel industry. Taking advantage of the deep water first identified by John Watt two hundred years earlier, the jetty has an alongside water depth of 95 feet.

The village of Fairlie changed considerably after the Second World War ended. Over the following years, many new homes were constructed, expanding the old village boundary to the north, east and south. The population also altered in its make-up as new employment opportunities arose in nearby towns such as Greenock and Irvine, and with the construction of two nuclear power stations at nearby Hunterston. These new sources of employment were very different to those available before the war, and many from far beyond Fairlie came to live in the village. Others chose to come to enjoy their retirement. Gradually the long-established village families have become outnumbered by the many incomers. Fairlie's historic social class structure dating from the shoreside mansions of the early nineteenth century has also largely disappeared. One result of all these changes is that few of those now living in the village know anything of Fairlie's Secret War.

The site of HM Anti-Submarine Experimental Establishment as viewed from Fairlie Bay in 2022. The older sandstone house on the far left is Dunora.

FURTHER READING

Bishop, Chris and Ross, David. *Submarines: World War I to the Present.* Amber Books, 2016.

Blair, Clay. *Hitler's U-Boat War: The Hunters, 1939–1942.* Modern Library, 2000.

Churchill, Winston. *The Second World War*, 6 vols. Cassell, 1949.

Costello, John and Hughes, Terry. *The Battle of the Atlantic.* Collins, 1977.

Friedman, Norman. *British Destroyers & Frigates: The Second World War and After.* Seaforth, 2006.

Hackmann, Willem. *Seek & Strike: Sonar, Anti-Submarine Warfare and the Royal Navy 1914–54.* HMSO, 1984.

Hartcup, Guy and Lovell, Bernard. *The Effect of Science on the Second World War.* Macmillan, 2016.

Henry, Chris. *Depth Charge: Royal Naval Mines, Depth Charges & Underwater Weapons 1914–1945.* Pen & Sword Military, 2005.

Lavery, Brian. *River-class Frigates and the Battle of the Atlantic: A Technical and Social History.* National Maritime Museum, 2006.

Lavery, Brian. *Shield of Empire: The Royal Navy in Scotland.* Birlinn, 2007.

Llewellyn-Jones, Malcolm. *The Royal Navy and Anti-Submarine Warfare, 1917–49*. Routledge, 2006.

Malmann Showell, Jak. *Weapons Used Against U-Boats during World War Two*. U-Boat Archive/HMSO, 2002.

McCallum, May. *Fast and Bonnie: A History of William Fife and Son Yachtbuilders*. John Donald, 1998.

Maxwell, Diana. *Listen Up!* Aberdour Cultural Association, 2015.

Milner, Marc. *The Battle of the Atlantic*. History Press, 2003.

National Archives, Kew. ADM 259. Admiralty: Anti-Submarine Experimental Establishment, later Underwater Detection Establishment: Technical and Progress Reports, 1914–90.

National Library of Scotland. *Navy List*. Various years.

Owen, David. *Anti-Submarine Warfare: An Illustrated History*. Seaforth, 2007.

Pawle, Gerald. *The Secret War 1939–45*. Loane Inc, 1957.

Robinson, Samuel. *Ocean Science and the British Cold War State*. Palgrave Macmillan, 2018.

Roskill, Stephen. *The War at Sea*, 3 vols. HMSO, 1954–61.

Terraine, John. *Business in Great Waters: The U-Boat Wars 1916–1945*. Mandarin, 1990.

PICTURE CREDITS

The author and publisher are grateful to the following for permission to reproduce images on the pages listed.

Courtesy of Bacon family: p. 98 top right

Courtesy of Binnie family: p. 88 left

© Castle Class Corvette Association: pp. 44, 61

Courtesy of Cazalet family: p. 83

Clyde Maritime Research Trust: p. 109 middle

© Clyde River Steamer Club: pp. 109 top, 114

Deutsches Bundesarchiv: p. 4

Deutsches U-Boot-Museum: p. 2

Devonport Naval Base Museum: p. 59 top

Graham Lappin Collection: p. 125 foot

James Hartery: p. 103

HMS Lapwing Association: p. 87 foot

© Imperial War Museum: pp. 6 [Q020379], 51 [A22031], 52 [A11948], 53 [A4570], 57 [31000], 60 [A33111], 64, 65 [FL518], 82 [SP1573], 111 [FL8598], 136 [A22010]

International Feldenkrais Federation: p. 122

Laboe Naval Memorial: p. 48

Largs & District Historical Society: pp. 32, 124, 125 top, 146

Library and Archives Canada: p. 42

© National Archives Kew: pp. 33, 54, 55 [ADM 239/612], 63 [ADM 259/171], 74 [ADM 199/2061], 104, 105 top [ADM 206/2], 107 [ADM 259/617]

© National Library of Scotland. Reproduced by permission of the Trustees: pp. 31 (chart), 81, 85, 100

© National Oceanographic Library University of Southampton: p. 98 top left

Redditch Local History Society: p. 117

Richard Cox Collection: p. 106

© Scottish Maritime Museum: pp. 21, 24, 26, 30, 144, 145

St Columba's Scottish Episcopal Church, Largs: p. 88 right

© Tirpitz Museum: p. 67

© University of St Andrews Libraries and Museums: p. 90 [ID JV-B818]

United States Library of Congress: p. 36

United States Navy Museum: p. 72

All other images are either from the author's collection or of indeterminate provenance. Every reasonable effort has been made prior to publication to establish provenance and contact copyright holders for permission to use images. The author will be pleased to rectify any omissions.

INDEX

153